FINE CANADIAN ART

AUCTION

D1178579

WEDNESDAY, MAY 25, 2005, 7PM
SHERATON WALL CENTRE HOTEL
1088 BURRARD STREET, VANCOUVER
PAVILION BALLROOM

EVENING HIGHLIGHT VERNISSAGE AT
GALERIE HEFFEL, MONTREAL
1840 RUE SHERBROOKE OUEST
WEDNESDAY, MAY 4, 7PM TO 9PM
PREVIEW THURSDAY, MAY 5, THROUGH
SATURDAY, MAY 7, 11AM TO 6PM

PREVIEW AT HEFFEL GALLERY, TORONTO
13 HAZELTON AVENUE
WEDNESDAY, MAY 11, THROUGH
SATURDAY, MAY 14, 11AM TO 6PM

PREVIEW AT HEFFEL GALLERY, VANCOUVER
SATURDAY, MAY 21, THROUGH
TUESDAY, MAY 24, 11AM TO 6PM
WEDNESDAY, MAY 25, 10AM TO 1PM

HEFFEL GALLERY
2247 GRANVILLE STREET, VANCOUVER
BRITISH COLUMBIA, CANADA V6H 3G1
TELEPHONE 604 732~6505, FAX 604 732~4245
TOLL FREE 800 528~9608
E~MAIL: MAIL@HEFFEL.COM
INTERNET: WWW.HEFFEL.COM

HEFFEL FINE ART AUCTION HOUSE

VANCOUVER • TORONTO • OTTAWA • MONTREAL

HEFFEL FINE ART AUCTION HOUSE

A Division of Heffel Gallery Limited

VANCOUVER
2247 Granville Street, Vancouver, BC V6H 3G1
Telephone 604 732~6505, Fax 604 732~4245
E~mail: mail@heffel.com, Internet: http://www.heffel.com

TORONTO
13 Hazelton Avenue, Toronto, Ontario M5R 2E1
Telephone 416 961~6505, Fax 416 961~4245

OTTAWA
104 Daly Avenue, Ottawa, Ontario K1N 6E7
Telephone 613 230~6505, Fax 413 674~3070

MONTREAL
1840 Rue Sherbrooke Ouest, Montreal, Quebec H3H 1E4
Telephone 514 939~6505, Fax 514 939~1100

CORPORATE BANK
Royal Bank of Canada, 1497 West Broadway
Vancouver, British Columbia V6H 1H7
Telephone 604 665~5731
Account #05680 003: 133 503 3, Swift Code: ROYccat2

BOARD OF DIRECTORS
Chairman *In Memoriam* ~ Kenneth Grant Heffel
President ~ David Kenneth John Heffel
Auctioneer License T83~3364318 and V05~110864
Vice President & Secretary ~ Robert Campbell Scott Heffel
Auctioneer License T83~3365303 and V05~110863

AUCTION PERSONNEL
Rosalin Te Omra ~ Assistant Director
of Fine Canadian Art and Research
Patsy Kim Heffel ~ Director of Accounting
Goran Urosevic ~ Director of Information Services
Alison Meredith ~ Director of Online Auction Sales
Judith Scolnik ~ Director of Toronto Office
Nina Kim ~ Manager of Eastern Division Offices
Andrew J.H. Gibbs ~ Director of Ottawa and Montreal Office
Bobby Ma ~ Director of Shipping and Framing
Deirdre Hofer ~ Director of Auction Price Index
Corinne Lefebvre ~ Manager of Montreal Office
Kendal Kendrick, Jill Meredith, Natasha Bissonauth, Jamey Petty,
Lauren Rotenberg, Kate Stephenson, Milan Vrekic ~ Support Staff
Martin Burian, Marjorie Cooper, Gary Cooper, Carla Giusti,
Debbie Heffel, Jennifer Heffel, Lindsay McAninch, Todd Shewfelt,
and Mike Tu ~ Auction Assistants
Jacques Barbeau, QC ~ Corporate Consultant
Paul S.O. Barbeau, Barbeau, Evans & Goldstein ~ Legal Advisor
Pami Buttar, Buttar Buttar ~ Corporate Accountant

CATALOGUE SUBSCRIPTIONS

Heffel Fine Art Auction House and Heffel Gallery Limited
regularly publish a variety of materials beneficial to the art
collector. An Annual Subscription entitles you to receive our
*Auction Catalogues, Auction Result Sheets, Gallery Exhibition
Invitations, Gallery Catalogues* and *Notices.* Our Annual
Subscription Form can be found on page 139 of this catalogue.

ISBN 0~9733998~2~1

PRINTING
Generation Printing, Vancouver

CATALOGUE PRODUCTION
Brian Goble ~ Director of Digital Imaging
Tessa Ohlendorf ~ Fine Photography and Digital Imaging, Toronto
Iris Schindel ~ Text Editor and Catalogue Layout

Heffel Gallery Limited is a member of the
Art Dealers Association of Canada

HEFFEL.COM DEPARTMENTS

FINE CANADIAN ART
canadianart@heffel.com

FINE PHOTOGRAPHY
photography@heffel.com

FINE AMERICAN ART
americanart@heffel.com

FINE EUROPEAN ART
europeanart@heffel.com

CANADIAN ART AT AUCTION INDEX
index@heffel.com

EMILY CARR WEBSITE PROJECT
kleewyck@heffel.com

SHIPPING
shipping@heffel.com

SUBSCRIPTIONS
subscriptions@heffel.com

MAP OF VANCOUVER PREVIEW AND AUCTION LOCATIONS

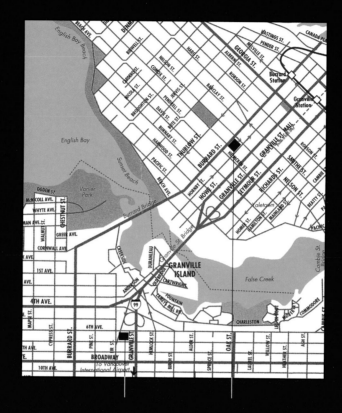

PREVIEW	AUCTION
2247 Granville Street, Vancouver	1088 Burrard Street, Vancouver
Telephone 604 732~6505	Hotel Telephone 604 331~1000
Toll Free 800 528~9608	Saleroom Cell 604 418~6505

Sheraton
WALL CENTRE
VANCOUVER
ITT

Please refer to page 132 for Montreal and Toronto preview locations

TABLE OF CONTENTS

SELLING AT AUCTION

Heffel Fine Art Auction House is a division of Heffel Gallery Limited. Together, our two operations offer individuals, collectors, corporations and public entities a full service firm for the successful de~acquisition of their artworks. Interested parties should contact us to arrange for a private and confidential appointment to discuss their preferred method of disposition and to analyse preliminary auction estimates, pre~sale reserves and consignment procedures. This service is offered free of charge.

If you are from out of town, or are unable to visit us at our premises, we would be pleased to assess the saleability of your artworks by mail or courier. Please provide us with photographic or facsimile reproductions of the artworks and information pertaining to title, artist, medium, size, date, provenance, etc. Representatives of our firm travel regularly to major Canadian cities to meet with prospective sellers and purchasers.

It is recommended that property for inclusion in our sale arrive at Heffel Fine Art Auction House at least 90 days prior to our auction. This allows time to photograph, research, catalogue, promote and complete any required work such as re~framing, cleaning or restoration. All property is stored free of charge until the auction; however, insurance is the Consignor's expense.

Consignors will receive, for completion, a *Consignment Agreement* and *Consignment Receipt,* which sets forth the terms and fees for our services. The *Seller's Commission* rates charged by Heffel Fine Art Auction House are as follows: 10% of the successful *Hammer Price* for each Lot sold for $7,500 and over; 15% for Lots sold for $2,500 to $7,499; and 25% for Lots sold for less than $2,500. Consignors are entitled to set a mutually agreed *Reserve* or minimum selling price on their artworks. Heffel Fine Art Auction House charges **no** *Seller's penalties* for artworks that do not achieve their *Reserve* price. However, we do charge a minimum commission of $100 plus a photography/cataloguing/internet posting charge of $100 for each Lot.

BUYING AT AUCTION

All items that are offered and sold by Heffel Fine Art Auction House are subject to our published *Terms and Conditions of Business*, our *Catalogue Terms* and any oral announcements made during the course of our sale. Heffel Fine Art Auction House charges a *Buyer's Premium* calculated at 15% of the *Hammer Price* of each Lot, plus applicable federal and provincial taxes.

If you are unable to attend our auction in person, you can bid by completing the *Absentee Bid Form* found on page 141 of this catalogue. Please note that all *Absentee Bid Forms* should be received by Heffel Fine Art Auction House at least 24 hours prior to the commencement of the sale.

Bidding by telephone, although limited, is available. Please make arrangements for this service well in advance of the sale. Telephone lines are assigned in order of the sequence in which requests are received. We also recommend that you leave an *Absentee Bid Form* that we will execute on your behalf in the event we are unable to reach you by telephone.

Payment must be made by: a) Bank Wire direct to our account, b) Certified Cheque or Bank Draft, unless otherwised arranged in advance with the Auction House, or c) a cheque accompanied by a current Letter of Credit from the Purchaser's bank which will guarantee the amount of the cheque. A cheque not guaranteed by a Letter of Credit must be cleared by the bank prior to purchases being released. We honour payment by VISA or Mastercard for purchases within North America up to $5,000 for online auction purchases and $25,000 for live auction purchases. Bank Wire payments should be made to Royal Bank of Canada, 1497 West Broadway, Vancouver, British Columbia V6H 1H7, Telephone 604 665~5731, Account #05680 003: 133 503 3, Swift Code: ROYccat2

GENERAL BIDDING INCREMENTS

Bidding typically begins below the low estimate and generally advances in the following bid increments:

$100 ~ 1,000	$50 INCREMENTS
$1,000 ~ 2,000	$100
$2,000 ~ 5,000	$250
$5,000 ~ 10,000	$500
$10,000 ~ 20,000	$1,000
$20,000 ~ 50,000	$2,500
$50,000~ 100,000	$5,000
$100,000 ~ 300,000	$10,000
$300,000 ~ 1,000,000	$25,000
$1,000,000 ~ 2,000,000	$50,000
$2,000,000 ~ 5,000,000	$100,000

FRAMING, RESTORATION AND SHIPPING

As a Consignor, it may be advantageous for you to have your artwork re~framed and/or cleaned and restored to enhance its saleability. As a Purchaser, your recently acquired artwork may demand a frame complementary to your collection. As a full service organization, we offer guidance and *in~house* expertise to facilitate these needs. Purchasers who acquire items that require local delivery or out~of~town shipping should refer to our *Shipping Form for Purchases* on page 140 of this publication. Please feel free to contact us to assist you in all of your requirements or to answer any of your related questions.

WRITTEN VALUATIONS AND APPRAISALS

Written valuations and appraisals for probate, insurance, family division and other purposes can be carried out in our offices or at your premises. Appraisal fees vary according to circumstances. If, within five years of the appraisal, valued or appraised artwork is consigned and sold through either Heffel Fine Art Auction House or Heffel Gallery Limited, the client will be refunded the appraisal fee, less incurred "out of pocket" expenses.

HEFFEL FINE ART AUCTION HOUSE

VANCOUVER • TORONTO • OTTAWA • MONTREAL

The Purchaser and the Consignor are hereby advised to read fully the *Terms and Conditions of Business* and *Catalogue Terms,* which set out and establish the rights and obligations of the Auction House, the Purchaser and the Consignor, and the terms by which the Auction House shall conduct the sale and handle other related matters. This information appears on pages 133 through 138 of this publication.

All Lots can be viewed on our Internet site at:

http://www.heffel.com

Please consult our online catalogue for information specifying which works will be displayed at each preview location and for additional cataloguing information at:

http://www.heffel.com/Auction/Index.asp

If you are unable to attend our auction, we produce a live webcast of our sale commencing at 6:50 PM PT. We do not offer real time Internet bidding for our live auctions, but we do accept Absentee and prearranged Telephone bids. Information on Absentee and Telephone bidding appears on pages 5 and 141 of this publication.

We recommend that you test your streaming video setup prior to our sale at:

http://www.heffel.tv

Our Estimates are in Canadian funds. Buying 1.00 Canadian dollar will cost 0.81 US dollar, 0.63 Euro or 0.44 British Pound as of our publication date.

FINE CANADIAN ART

CATALOGUE

SALE WEDNESDAY, MAY 25, 2005, 7PM, VANCOUVER

1

1 W.J. (WALTER JOSEPH) PHILLIPS
ASA CPE CSPWC RCA 1884 ~ 1963

Rocky Mountains

watercolour on paper, signed and dated 1952
17 x 18 in, 43.2 x 45.7 cm

PROVENANCE:
Private Collection, Ontario

LITERATURE:
Duncan Campbell Scott, *Walter J. Phillips*, 1947, page 26

Phillips first traveled to the Rocky Mountains from his home in Winnipeg in 1926. In 1940 he was asked to be an instructor at the Banff Summer School, and it was the first of 20 summers he spent teaching there. Phillips loved Banff, and built a house on Tunnel Mountain in 1946, often heading into the surrounding landscape to paint. He wrote that "Mountains are spectacular...[and] when the light is right ~ there are golden days that are indescribably beautiful ~ there are pictures everywhere."

ESTIMATE: $6,000 ~ 9,000

2

2 W.J. (WALTER JOSEPH) PHILLIPS
ASA CPE CSPWC RCA 1884 ~ 1963

The Cove

watercolour on paper, signed and dated 1955 and on verso titled
17 1/2 x 18 1/2 in, 44.4 x 47 cm

PROVENANCE:
Private Collection, Ontario

LITERATURE:
W.J. Phillips, *Wet Paint*, an unpublished manuscript, pages 46 ~ 47

Phillips is considered to be a master of watercolour. In his manuscript *Wet Paint*, he spoke of the challenges of the medium: "Watercolour painting is notoriously difficult, so much depends on directness and speed, and certainty of intention...The most admirable method is that by which each wash of color, large or small, is never disturbed." His watercolours are noted for delicacy of detail, fresh clear light and absolute certainty of technique.

ESTIMATE: $4,000 ~ 6,000

3   W.J. (WALTER JOSEPH) PHILLIPS
ASA CPE CSPWC RCA 1884 ~ 1963

The Waterfront, Alert Bay, BC
colour woodcut, signed and editioned 67 (edition of 300), 1928
6 1/4 x 8 3/4 in, 15.9 x 22.2 cm

PROVENANCE:
Private Collection, Ontario

LITERATURE:
Roger Boulet, *The Tranquility and the Turbulence*, 1981, reproduced page 98
Roger Boulet, *Walter J. Phillips: The Complete Graphic Works*, 1981, page 294, reproduced page 295

This print appeared in the 1928 portfolio *The Canadian Scene,* which included an introduction by Martin Hardie, the Keeper of Prints at the Victoria and Albert Museum, London, and a dissertation by the artist on the prints and their subject matter. This portfolio consists of seven prints, each in an edition of 300, with 50 portfolios destined for the British market and 50 for the American market. Boulet quotes Phillips on the scene in Alert Bay: "This is a view from the board~walk in the white quarter, looking over Johnstone Strait. The few shacks which are roofed with cedar 'shakes', and the wharf, belong to an affable Chinese merchant named Jim King."

ESTIMATE: $1,500 ~ 2,000

3

4   W.J. (WALTER JOSEPH) PHILLIPS
ASA CPE CSPWC RCA 1884 ~ 1963

Siwash House Posts, Tsatsisnukomi, BC
colour woodcut, signed and editioned 67 (edition of 300), 1928
8 1/8 x 6 1/4 in, 20.6 x 15.9 cm

PROVENANCE:
Private Collection, Ontario

LITERATURE:
Roger Boulet, *The Tranquility and the Turbulence,* 1981, page 99, reproduced page 99

Roger Boulet, *Walter J. Phillips: The Complete Graphic Works,* 1981, page 296, reproduced page 297

This is the second print from the 1928 portfolio *The Canadian Scene.* Boulet quotes Phillips's comments on the village: "Late in the afternoon we came to Tsatsisnukomi. The gleaming beach, shaped like the new moon, was fringed with a row of buildings, mostly weathered grey...We stayed awhile the next day, until the wind made the anchorage uncomfortable, but I had time to make pencil drawings of some of the more grotesque carvings, and a watercolour of the beach and part of the village, with two house~posts in the foreground, each representing a bear suckling a wolf." This is the woodcut produced from that watercolour.

ESTIMATE: $1,500 ~ 2,000

4

5

5 KATHLEEN MOIR MORRIS
ARCA BHHG 1893 ~ 1986

Market Day, Ottawa
oil on panel, signed, circa 1925
10 1/4 x 13 3/4 in, 26 x 35.6 cm

PROVENANCE:
Galerie Walter Klinkhoff Inc., Montreal
Private Collection, Montreal

LITERATURE:
Dorota Kozinska, *Kathleen Morris: Retrospective Exhibition*,
Galerie Walter Klinkhoff Inc., September 2003, page 5
Barbara Meadowcroft, *Painting Friends*, 1999, page 86

EXHIBITED:
Galerie Walter Klinkhoff Inc., Montreal, *Kathleen Morris, RCA*, Loan
Exhibition, June 1976, catalogue #38

Morris lived in Ottawa from 1923 to 1929 with her mother Eliza. Morris
had a nervous ailment that impaired her speech, but she was nevertheless
very confident due to "the intelligent support and boundless love given
her by her mother and brothers. Mrs. Morris devoted her life to her,"
according to Meadowcroft. Eric Brown, Director of the National Gallery
in Ottawa during that time, was a supporter, and the National Gallery
acquired one of her works. Brown was instrumental in the inclusion of
many Canadian artists in the important Wembley exhibition in England
in 1924, and Morris was one of them.

An aspect of beauty in this painting is its luscious colour. Kozinska writes,
"Her art can be compared to the work of the Nabis, a group of mainly
French painters active in the 1890s, whose works were influenced by
Gauguin's expressive use of colour and rhythmic pattern. Like them,
Morris translated her surroundings in an intuitive manner, guided by
colour more than form."

ESTIMATE: $35,000 ~ 45,000

6 SYBIL ANDREWS

CPE 1898 ~ 1992

Flower Girls

linocut in 4 colours, signed, titled and editioned 28/60
9 3/4 x 8 1/2 in, 24.8 x 21.6 cm

PROVENANCE:
Private Collection, Toronto

LITERATURE:
Stephen Coppel, *Linocuts of the Machine Age*, 1995, page 114,
reproduced page 114
Peter White, *Sybil Andrews*, Glenbow Museum, 1982, reproduced full
page colour, page 40

Early impressions of this print are on buff oriental laid paper, while later
impressions are on thicker oriental paper. Coppel writes: "The repeated
angular shapes and colour patterns give dynamic energy to this study of
movement."

ESTIMATE: $10,000 ~ 12,000

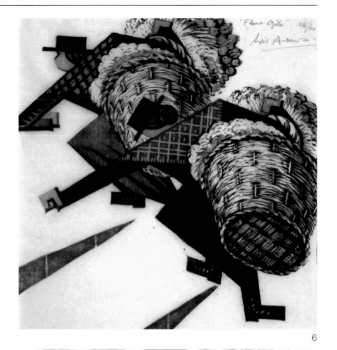

6

 7 **SYBIL ANDREWS**

CPE 1898 ~ 1992

Michaelmas

linocut in 4 colours, signed, titled and editioned *TP.1*, 1935
12 x 8 3/4 in, 30.5 x 22.2 cm

LITERATURE:
Morning Post, July 11, 1935, page 14
Stephen Coppel, *Linocuts of the Machine Age*, 1995, page 114,
reproduced page 115, SA #33
Peter White, *Sybil Andrews*, Glenbow Museum, 1982, reproduced full
page colour, page 41

EXHIBITED:
Redfern Gallery, London, catalogue #8, same image, 1935
The Los Angeles Museum, *The Fifteenth International Print Makers
Exhibition under the auspices of the Print Makers Society of California*, same
image, 1935
Baillieu Allard's Gallery, Melbourne, Australia, *Exhibition of Linocuts from
the Redfern Gallery*, same image, 1937
Gainsborough Galleries, Johannesberg, South Africa, *Exhibition of
Handcrafts*, same image, 1945

A 1935 review in the *Morning Post* stated: "Miss Andrews and Mr. Power
easily hold first place in the Linocut section [of London 1935 (Redfern)],
she, with the remarkable '*Michaelmas*' and the exceedingly dramatic
'*Storm*', his '*Air Raid*' and '*Concerto*', each in its own way displaying
extraordinary technical skill."

This print is an edition of 60 plus 2 trial proofs. Early impressions of this fine
print are on buff oriental laid tissue ~ later printings are on thickish oriental
laid paper. As this is TP.1, it is an early printing on oriental laid tissue. Please
note that this work is unframed.

ESTIMATE: $7,000 ~ 9,000

7

8

8   **DAVID BROWN MILNE**
1882 ~ 1953

Clouds, Blue Sky, Six Mile Lake, Muskoka, Ontario

oil on canvas, signed and on verso titled by others *Clouds at Sunset, Six Mile Lake* (the *Catalogue Raisonné* titles the work *Clouds, Blue Sky* based on the Massey Inventory), 1933
12 x 14 1/4 in, 30.5 x 36.2 cm

PROVENANCE:
Milne sale to Vincent Massey, 1934; Laing Galleries, Toronto, 1958
Roberts Gallery, Toronto, 1961; Acquired by the present Private Toronto Collector, 1961

LITERATURE:
David Milne Jr. and David P. Silcox, *David B. Milne: Catalogue Raisonné of the Paintings Volume 2: 1929~1953*, 1998, reproduced page 580, catalogue #303.26

EXHIBITED:
Laing Galleries, Toronto, 1958
Roberts Gallery, Toronto, 1961

The period 1933~1934 was one of turbulence for Milne. He had recently separated from his wife Patsy and left the village of Palgrave which had provided subjects for a long period of painting. He traveled to Six Mile Lake in the late spring and spent most of the summer and fall camping. The lack of a proper studio or cabin meant that he chose to work on small canvases which allowed him to address a series of pictorial problems that interested him. These works rely on his exceptional skills as a draughtsman and his sure sense of the dynamics of composition. This work, which was part of a large collection of paintings sold to the Massey family in 1934, was likely done in the summer or early fall of 1933 and signed later when it was sent to Vincent Massey. An exciting image, it seems to explode with energy in the sky, the grey area of the water serving as a foil to the drawing of the land and the brilliant sky. The use of a warm ground colour for the whole composition unites the image beneath the powerful drawing. The image is a succinct and vivid distillation of Milne's experience of the Six Mile Lake landscape ~ the spare, rocky shore and the riotous cloudscape of the sky. The great joy of this image is the fact that he is able to accurately suggest the experience of the landscape through colour and form which only tangentially refers to the reality of nature. *Clouds, Blue Sky* is clearly a work of art, an aesthetic experience, not an attempt to simply depict the real world.

ESTIMATE: $45,000 ~ 65,000

9

9   TOM (THOMAS JOHN) THOMSON
G7 OSA   1877 ~ 1917

Stormy Weather
watercolour on paper, signed
9 1/2 x 14 in, 24.1 x 35.6 cm

PROVENANCE:
Estate of the Artist; John Thomson; Lottie Gilchrist, 1917
By descent to Duncan Gilchrist, Winnipeg; Sotheby & Co. (Canada) Ltd., *Important Canadian Paintings, Drawings, Watercolours, Books and Prints of the 19th and 20th Centuries*, May 12 ~13, 1975, Lot 17; Private Collection, Toronto

This work will be included in Joan Murray's forthcoming catalogue raisonné on the artist's work.

ESTIMATE: $10,000 ~ 15,000

10   DAVID BROWN MILNE
1882 ~ 1953

The Last of Autumn, New York
oil on canvas, on verso inscribed incorrectly by Patsy Milne: *MFM, per May F Milne, Hudson River, 1913*; also inscribed by others on the Morris Gallery label: *Hudson River 1913, May Milne Collection*, circa 1908 ~ 1910
17 x 14 in, 43.2 x 35.6 cm

PROVENANCE:
Patsy Milne; Jerrold Morris Gallery, Toronto; Kenneth G. Heffel Fine Art Inc., Vancouver, 1980; Kyle's Gallery, Victoria, BC; Private Collection, Victoria; By descent to the present Private Collection, Ontario

LITERATURE:
David Milne Jr. and David P. Silcox, *David Milne, Catalogue Raisonné, Volume 1: 1882 ~ 1928*, 1998, page 15, reproduced page 32, catalogue #102.55

10

EXHIBITED:
McLaughlin Library, Oshawa, Ontario, 1962

The Milne *Catalogue Raisonné* states: "The location and date inscribed by Patsy Milne are inaccurate". The *Catalogue Raisonné* titles the work *The Last of Autumn, New York* and dates this important early rare painting circa 1908 ~ 1910.

ESTIMATE: $15,000 ~ 20,000

11

11   DAVID BROWN MILNE
1882 ~ 1953

Canoe and Fireplace, Six Mile Lake, Ontario
oil on canvas, 1933
12 1/8 x 16 1/8 in, 30.8 x 41 cm

PROVENANCE:
Milne sale to Massey, 1934
Hart Massey, Port Hope, Ontario
Morris Gallery, Toronto
Private Collection, Toronto

LITERATURE:
David Milne Jr. and David P. Silcox, *David B. Milne: Catalogue Raisonné of the Paintings Volume 2: 1929 ~ 1953*, 1998, page 567, reproduced page 572, catalogue #303.6

After leaving Palgrave, Milne discovered Six Mile Lake in 1933 while exploring with fellow artists Don and Florence Houston. The lake was an isolated spot about three kilometres from Big Chute in Muskoka, and in September of that year he began constructing a cabin there. To reach the cabin he had to go partially by canoe and by foot. Milne liked to retreat into nature and live in simple circumstances. In 1920 he had built a cabin on Alander Mountain in New York to work in, compelled by the idea of having "endless painting material just outside my door". Six Mile Lake surrounded Milne with inspiration once more, and he remained there until 1939. The *Catalogue Raisonné* states, "Milne's subject matter at Six Mile Lake led him back, naturally, to the kind of landscape that he had known in the western Adirondacks and at Temagami: bush and trees, lakes and rivers, granite rock, islands, points, and headlands, along with whatever still~life subjects caught his eye around the cabin."

ESTIMATE: $45,000 ~ 65,000

12

12 DAVID BROWN MILNE
1882 ~ 1953

Wooded Hills III, Baptiste Lake (Wooded Hills ~ Brown Version)

watercolour on paper, on verso titled, dated March, 1951 on the watercolour paper and inscribed by Duncan on the backing: *David Milne, Wooded Hills (brown version March 1951) $185 c/o Douglas Duncan, 3 Charles St. W, Toronto, 1951*
14 1/2 x 21 1/2 in, 36.8 x 54.6 cm

PROVENANCE:
Duncan/Picture Loan (possibly through the Women's Committee, Art Gallery of Toronto), 1951
By descent to the present Private Collection, Toronto

LITERATURE:
David Milne Jr. and David P. Silcox, *David B. Milne: Catalogue Raisonné of the Paintings Volume 2: 1929 ~ 1953*, 1998, reproduced page 965, catalogue #503.10

EXHIBITED:
Art Gallery of Toronto, 1951

For most of David Milne's career he pursued more than one area of artistic expression, printmaking or watercolour paired with oil painting. These other forms of artistic expression were not in any way inferior to one another and his achievements in each were exceptional. Indeed, many regard David Milne as Canada's greatest watercolourist. It was this medium that became his most important form of expression in the last several years of his life. These late watercolours are, at times, almost ethereal, seemingly more wished upon the paper than painted. In images such as *Wooded Hills III*, one of four essays that Milne made of this Baptiste Lake subject in February and March of 1951, he drenched the paper in water and allowed the pigment to blossom across the page. These works are remarkable achievements in watercolour painting. Milne considered the subject in his mind and when he was ready he painted quickly and with exceptional daring and precision. These images are not forgiving of mistakes; it is very difficult to take back a colour that is placed incorrectly. The subject is not a momentous one, but in Milne's hands it provides that visual punch that makes for an exciting and vital work of art.

ESTIMATE: $25,000 ~ 35,000

13

13   CORNELIUS DAVID KRIEGHOFF

1815 ~ 1872

An Incident in a Winter Blizzard

oil on canvas, signed, circa 1860
11 x 20 in, 27.9 x 50.8 cm

PROVENANCE:
Private Collection, Cologne, Germany

LITERATURE:
J. Russell Harper, *Krieghoff*, 1979, page 78, similar work entitled *Run off the Road in a Blizzard* reproduced page 79
Dennis Reid, *Krieghoff / Images of Canada*, 1999, page 148, similar work entitled *A Winter Incident* reproduced page 242

Krieghoff was an immensely successful artist who made his living catering to the merchant and military classes in Montreal and Quebec in the mid~nineteenth century. Born in Germany, he landed in the United States in 1835, then settled in Montreal in 1840, and was soon among the most important artists working in the young British colony of The Province of Canada. His keen sense of observation and skills as a painter made his canvases ideal souvenirs of Canadian life for those who returned to England and Europe. This fine canvas is a superb example of his considerable skills as a storyteller and his ability to control large areas of colour. Although the predominant colour of this work is grey, Krieghoff, through the judicious use of brighter accents and the warmth of the grey itself, conveys a scene which is gently comic rather than catastrophic. The handling of the snow, which is, in many ways, the major subject of this painting, is particularly engaging ~ the way the snow settles on the branches and fence in the left foreground, the drifts of snow and the falling snow itself all suggest the artist's deep familiarity with his subject. Krieghoff has been careful to isolate the main action through the use of a pool of light at the centre of the composition and we can clearly see how unhappy the driver of the overturned sleigh is with the other traveler, but it is also fair to say that there is little sense of urgency in the situation. Krieghoff has exploited the picturesque and anecdotal aspects of his subject to advantage; we see and are amused by the situation rather than being directly involved. Clearly, Krieghoff is reveling in his skills of composition and paint handling. It is an image that is immensely satisfying both intellectually and aesthetically, and one can easily see it as emblematic of the habitant life in French Canada.

ESTIMATE: $100,000 ~ 150,000

14

14 CORNELIUS DAVID KRIEGHOFF

1815 ~ 1872

Sleighs Racing in Front of the Citadel, Quebec

oil on canvas, signed and on verso inscribed on the canvas:
*Scott Marsden, 2 Victoria Square Montreal, Quebec Heights of
Abraham, Sold to General Williams*
8 3/4 x 13 in, 22.2 x 33 cm

PROVENANCE:
Scott Marsden, Montreal
General Williams
Mr. Gilbert Labine, Toronto
By descent to a Private Estate, Toronto/Vancouver
Private Collection, Toronto

LITERATURE:
Dennis Reid, *Krieghoff / Images of Canada*, essay by Ramsay Cook, Art
Gallery of Ontario, 1999, page 162, similar work reproduced page 22,
plate #21 and front cover

Krieghoff depicted all aspects of habitant life, and although their life
was challenging, it was also full of exuberant pleasures, such as horse
and sleigh racing. Cook writes, "This was a pastime that since the
eighteenth century the authorities had attempted to curb without much
success. Organized horse racing, which grew in popularity in the
nineteenth century, came to Quebec with the British." Habitants often
conducted their contests of speed on Sundays and holidays, and writers
of the times even complained of racing near churches. This painting, set
against the Citadel and a glorious colourful sky, brilliantly recreates this
exhilarating sport.

ESTIMATE: $75,000 ~ 95,000

15

15   CLARENCE ALPHONSE GAGNON
RCA   1881 ~ 1942

Blueberry Picking

tempera on board, stamped *Atelier Gagnon* and on verso
certified by Lucile Rodier Gagnon #644, Paris 1946, circa
1928 ~ 1933
7 3/4 x 8 1/2 in, 19.7 x 21.6 cm

PROVENANCE:
Private Collection, Ontario

LITERATURE:
Louis Hémon, *Maria Chapdelaine*, illustrations by Clarence Gagnon,
1933, same scene reproduced page 73, now in the McMichael Canadian
Art Collection

David Wistow, *The McMichael Canadian Art Collection*, 1989, page 127

This extraordinary work is closely related to an almost identical Gagnon
painting in the McMichael Canadian Art Collection, which is reproduced
in the book *Maria Chapdelaine*. Wistow writes that Gagnon "is best
known today for the illustrations he created for *Maria Chapdelaine*. The
now~famous novel ~ written in 1914 by Frenchman Louis Hémon who

had immigrated to Canada ~ tells the story of a young girl growing up in rural Quebec. Scenes of bread baking, blueberry picking, hay cutting and maple syrup gathering, played against rolling farmland and dramatic seasonal changes, evoke an age~old way of life untrammeled by the modern world...These images are so unforgettable because Gagnon clearly holds the inhabitants in deepest respect; he grew up in late nineteenth~century rural Quebec, north of Montreal, and he knew their way of life intimately...It is...the seven hard years he devoted to *Maria Chapdelaine* that have secured Gagnon his place in the annals of Canadian art."

In this softly lit painting glowing with colour, Gagnon's habitants work in an atmosphere of harmony with the natural world around them.

ESTIMATE: $30,000 ~ 40,000

16

16 MANNER OF CORNELIUS KRIEGHOFF
The Habitant Farm
oil on canvas, bears signature
9 x 12 in, 22.9 x 30.5 cm

PROVENANCE:
Private Collection, Toronto

ESTIMATE: $3,000 ~ 4,000

17 CORNELIUS DAVID KRIEGHOFF
1815 ~ 1872

Habitant with Pipe
oil on canvas, signed, circa 1855
11 1/2 x 9 in, 29.2 x 22.9 cm

PROVENANCE:
Sir Casimir Gzowski, Toronto
University Book Service, Toronto
O.W. Hendry, Toronto (purchased from University Book Service in 1934)
Private Collection, Chatham and Toronto, Ontario
By descent to the present Private Collection, Peterborough, Ontario

EXHIBITED:
Art Gallery of Toronto, remnants of a label on verso

The invoice from the University Book Service, dated October 10th, 1934 and a letter from the University Book Service to Oscar Hendry, dated July 17th, 1936 accompany this lot. The letter outlines the provenance of the painting and states that it was examined by Dr. Marius Barbeau (among others), who planned to include it in the revised edition of his book on the artist.

ESTIMATE: $25,000 ~ 35,000

17

18

18 PAUL PEEL
OSA RCA 1860 ~ 1892

The Fisher Boy
oil on canvas, signed, dated 1881 and inscribed *P.A.*
22 x 18 in, 55.9 x 45.7 cm

PROVENANCE:
Canon Fred Whitley, Montreal
By descent to the present Private Collection, Victoria

LITERATURE:
Victoria Baker, *Paul Peel: A Retrospective, 1860 ~ 1892*, London Regional
Art Gallery, 1986, page 26

Peel had completed his studies at the Pennsylvania Academy in the
United States in 1880, and many of its graduates pursued studies in Paris,
inspiring others to follow suit. By May of 1881, Peel had joined the
American artists' colony at Pont~Aven in Brittany, France. The inscription
P.A. on this painting most probably refers to Pont~Aven. The colony,
established as early as the 1840s, was based in Brittany during the
summers and Paris in the winter. Baker writes that "Brittany held special
appeal for artists whose taste for traditional rural themes and peasant
imagery, cultivated by the painters of the Barbizon school, was satisfied by
the colourfully~costumed Breton inhabitants whose lifestyle and
customs were in many ways more medieval than modern." The Breton
people were friendly and would readily pose for artists, and Peel seems
charmed by the sunny disposition of this boy. The bright, direct light in
this exceptional painting is typical of the work Peel did at this time. He
uses the flat background surface in this work to reflect light like a mirror,
making the figure stand out strongly in contrast. Peel returned to Brittany
annually over the next decade, with the Breton peasant emerging as one of
his leading pictorial motifs.

ESTIMATE: $55,000 ~ 65,000

19

19   CORNELIUS DAVID KRIEGHOFF
1815 ~ 1872

Indian Family Around a Campfire with Birchbark Tepee and Canoe
oil on canvas, signed, circa 1858
14 1/4 x 21 in, 36.2 x 53.3 cm

PROVENANCE:
Acquired from the Artist by Thomas Dillon Tims, Ottawa
Mrs. D.A. Coste (Harriet Tims), Niagara Falls
Mrs. S.A. Morse (Isabelle Coste), Chatham

LITERATURE:
Dennis Reid, *Krieghoff: Images of Canada*, 1999, page 227, similar work reproduced page 194

Krieghoff's paintings with First Nations subject matter date from 1847, when one first appeared in a Montreal Gallery of Pictures exhibition. Three years later, native imagery in his work had become almost as important as habitants, and about one third of his known work is composed of this subject matter. While in Montreal he often depicted Mohawk and Iroquois natives from the Caughnawaga reserve. When he moved to Quebec City in 1853, Micmac and Montagnais peoples were camped at Indian Cove on the Levis River and the Huron village at Lorette was nearby. This work dates from this time period, as Reid writes: "Only after his move to Quebec City did he paint genre scenes that included Indian figures." These tableaux~like scenes depicted Indians as romantic figures, and in this fine painting, a family group communes peacefully with each other in an idyllic landscape. As is typical for this period, the figures are small against the larger backdrop of nature. Reid writes: "Krieghoff felt an affinity with these forest people, who had often acted as his guides on hunting expeditions...his image of the Indian conveyed a harmonious vitality." Clearly Krieghoff's vision was that of a people unspoiled by civilization.

A 1992 photograph certificate of authenticity signed by Walter Klinkhoff accompanies this work.

ESTIMATE: $70,000 ~ 90,000

20   HELEN GALLOWAY MCNICOLL

ARCA RBA 1879 ~ 1915

Mother and Child Picking Berries

oil on canvas, signed, circa 1911
22 x 21 in, 55.9 x 53.3 cm

PROVENANCE:
W. Scott and Sons, Montreal
Private Collection, Montreal
By descent to the present Private Collection, Vancouver

LITERATURE:
Natalie Luckyj, *Helen McNicoll*, Art Gallery of Ontario, 1999,
pages 15 and 25

EXHIBITED:
Art Association of Montreal, remnants of label on verso

Luckyj writes that "Helen McNicoll's luminous and intimate paintings
celebrate the separate world of women and children and the rituals of
everyday life that today appear idyllic." This extraordinary work, like the
painting *By the Lake*, also in this auction, is striking in its rich colour and
very assured and natural use of outdoor light. McNicoll's training at the
Slade School of Art in London from 1902 ~ 1904 brought her into contact
with pleinairism, a style of painting that emphasized the feeling of open
air and atmosphere much favoured by French and British impressionists.
Luckyj writes that "[a] 'new romantic/atmospheric' style permeated the
Slade School, which advocated a naturalism and evocation of mood, and
rejected the sentimentality and story~telling of late Victorian art." After
this, McNicoll traveled to Paris for three months, opening a studio and
touring through the countryside looking for painting subjects. By 1905,
McNicoll had returned to England to St. Ives on the Cornish coast. Here
she met the painter Dorothea Sharp, and they traveled and painted
together, visiting artist colonies in Brittany, Grès~sur~Loing and Italy.

The painting has a very evocative mood of gentleness and delight in
nature with the mother lifting her child so that she may pick the choicest
berries herself. McNicoll shows her mastery of light in the dappling of
light along the leaves, the heat haze in the background and the
luminousness of the child's skin. Adding to the beauty of the work is the
lush patterning of leaves and branches, the soft draperies of their dresses,
and the luscious greens and mauves of the paint. This work is a romantic
celebration of feminine sensibility and a masterful plein air painting.

ESTIMATE: $60,000 ~ 80,000

21

21 JOHN GOODWIN LYMAN
CAS CGP FRSA 1886 ~ 1967

Vacation / Vacances

oil on canvas, signed and on verso signed, titled and
inscribed with the artist's address on the artist's label, 1950
27 1/4 x 30 in, 69.2 x 76.2 cm

PROVENANCE:
Dominion Gallery, Montreal

EXHIBITED:
Montreal Museum of Fine Arts, *The Eastern Group of Painters*, January 28
to February 17, 1950
Dominion Gallery, Montreal, *John Lyman*, October 5 to 22, 1955
Musée du Quebec, Quebec City, *John Lyman Retrospective*, November 23
to December 19, 1966, traveling exhibition, catalogue #161

ESTIMATE: $18,000 ~ 22,000

22 SUZANNE DUQUET
QMG 1917 ~

Adèle

oil on canvas, signed, circa 1949
39 x 24 in, 99 x 61 cm

PROVENANCE:
Gilles Tremblay, Montreal
Private Collection, Quebec

LITERATURE:
Germain Lefebvre, *Suzanne Duquet, Volet Figuratif 1939 ~ 1954*, The
Montreal Museum of Fine Arts, 1976 ~ 1977, reproduced front cover

EXHIBITED:
The Montreal Museum of Fine Arts, *Suzanne Duquet, Volet Figuratif 1939 ~
1954*, 1976 ~ 1977, catalogue #23

Suzanne Duquet received her formal training at the Montreal École des
beaux~arts in the 1930s and is considered to be a member of the Quebec
Modern Group. She taught for over 30 years at the École des beaux~arts.
Although she painted still life and landscape, a central theme in her work
was figurative subject matter, which was the theme of her exhibition at
Montreal's Museum of Fine Arts. They were mostly women, for as she
wrote, "I could not afford to hire models so I would ask my friends to pose
for me. It was much more difficult to convince my male friends to assume
this role. Moreover, the elegance of women's attitudes, gestures, hair or
clothing was a better source of inspiration for my artistic motifs."

ESTIMATE: $10,000 ~ 15,000

22

23

24

23   HENRIETTA MABEL MAY

ARCA BHHG CGP RPS 1884 ~ 1971

Portrait of the Artist's Sister

oil on canvas, circa 1925
30 1/4 x 26 in, 76.8 x 66 cm

PROVENANCE:
Estate of the Artist
Private Collection, Vancouver

When Mabel May returned to Montreal from Europe in 1913 she rented a studio but continued to live with her parents and her sister Lillian. In the summer she painted and played golf with Lillian at Hudson Heights. In 1950 Mabel and Lillian moved to Vancouver where their sister Queenie White lived. As Lillian spent much time with Mabel, it is possible that she is the sister represented in this work.

ESTIMATE: $6,000 ~ 8,000

24   HENRIETTA MABEL MAY

ARCA BHHG CGP RPS 1884 ~ 1971

Portrait of the Artist's Mother

oil on canvas, circa 1925
26 1/4 x 21 in, 66.7 x 53.3 cm

PROVENANCE:
Estate of the Artist
Private Collection, Vancouver

LITERATURE:
Barbara Meadowcroft, *Painting Friends*, 1999, page 92

Mabel May's mother was Evelyn Henrietta Walker, and Mabel May was the fifth of her ten children. Meadowcroft writes: "Mabel took up painting in her teens, but she postponed her professional training until her mid~twenties to help with the younger children." At the age of twenty~five she entered the classes of William Brymner at the Montreal Museum of Fine Arts.

ESTIMATE: $4,000 ~ 6,000

25 HELEN GALLOWAY MCNICOLL
ARCA RBA   1879 ~ 1915

By the Lake
oil on canvas, signed and on verso titled
on the Watson Gallery label, Record #2976
circa 1911
20 x 24 in, 50.8 x 61 cm

PROVENANCE:
Watson Art Galleries, Montreal
By descent to the present Private Collection, Ontario

LITERATURE:
Natalie Luckyj, *Helen McNicoll: A Canadian Impressionist*,
Art Gallery of Ontario, 1999, page 57

Helen McNicoll was from a wealthy family in Montreal who
encouraged her art career, enabling her to travel to Britain and France
to study. McNicoll spent two years at the renowned Slade School of Art
at the University of London, where she was influenced by the British
impressionists and exhibitions of impressionist work, both French
and British.

McNicoll's London residence was at 6 Gordon Square in central London,
which was near the Slade and the British Museum as well as commercial
galleries. London was an exciting centre, with exhibitions such as the
Grafton Galleries' show of 300 French impressionist works from the
collection of the French art dealer Durand~Ruel in 1905, which McNicoll
no doubt would have seen. While in England, McNicoll befriended
British painter Dorothea Sharp. They traveled and painted together, as
well as sharing studio space. A childhood illness had rendered McNicoll
deaf, and Sharp helped McNicoll in gaining permission to use people as
models in her outdoor paintings, as well as liberating her from the
unwanted attention she would have had from painting alone in public
places such as this seashore scene. McNicoll spent most of her adult life
abroad, and traveled through England, France and Italy.

McNicoll's absorption with the theme of women and children began
very early, and she painted this subject matter throughout her life. The
advent of impressionism had opened up a new world of light, colour
and subject matter that suited domestic themes. Luckyj writes that
"McNicoll and her contemporaries...using images of contemporary life
centred on the domestic world of women and children, could now
actively participate in the making of a modernist aesthetic that
legitimized what Griselda Pollock has called the 'spaces of femininity'."
Here, McNicoll celebrates the children's simple pleasure in their
physical engagement with the water. This idyllic and nostalgic scene,
bathed in radiant light, captures the innocent world of late Victorian
and Edwardian times.

ESTIMATE: $50,000 ~ 60,000

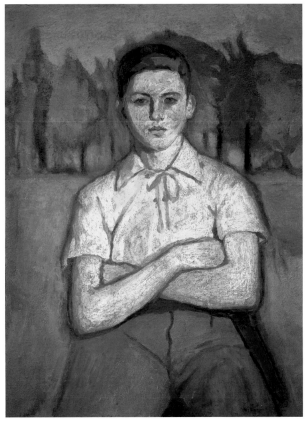

26

26 EMILY COONAN
BHHG   1885 ~ 1971

Portrait Of Frank Coonan, Jr.
oil on canvas, signed
29 1/4 x 22 in, 74.3 x 55.9 cm

PROVENANCE:
Masters Gallery, Calgary; Private Collection, Toronto

LITERATURE:
Barbara Meadowcroft, *Painting Friends*, 1999, pages 109 and 110

Emily Coonan was associated with the Beaver Hall Group of painters.
Meadowcroft writes, "Emily Coonan was absolutely dedicated to her work.
For most of her life, she painted at home, in the house she shared with her
father, sister Eva, brother Frank, and Frank's son Frankie (b. 1930)."

ESTIMATE: $20,000 ~ 25,000

27

27 ALBERT HENRY ROBINSON
ARCA RCA 1881 ~ 1956

St. Tite des Caps
oil on canvas, signed, titled and dated 1928
22 x 26 in, 55.9 x 66 cm

PROVENANCE:
George H. Robinson, Toronto, brother of the Artist
By descent to the present Private Collection, Ontario

LITERATURE:
A.Y. Jackson, *A Painter's Country*, 1958, page 82

EXHIBITED:
Laing Fine Art Galleries Ltd, Toronto, label on verso

St. Tite des Caps on the north shore of the St. Lawrence, east of Quebec City, was a favourite painting spot for many artists ~ Jackson, Hewton and Banting to name only three. Robinson visited it and other villages with Jackson on a number of occasions. Of their approach to these villages, Jackson wrote, "Robinson and I, in our paintings, accepted all the contemporary types of buildings which made the old Quebec villages a jumble", suggesting that both were ready to work with what was before them rather than inventing architecture. This painting, which might be the quintessential Quebec scene is, however, far from a jumble. The more one looks at it the more one realizes how carefully Robinson has planned the composition. The whole work can be effectively divided into quarters with the church and its spire providing the main vertical axis and the tops of the snowdrifts the horizontal. Robinson has placed the human elements ~ the two men sawing and the two children ~ in the foreground and middle ground of the lower half of the composition. The figure at the far right provides a visual link between the two halves of the composition and allows us to move into the space. Rather surprisingly, given the season, it reads as a warm image rather than a cold one. This has been accomplished by the immediacy of the human figures but also by the use of a warm pink that appears throughout the composition and balances the cooler greys and blues. This blue/pink opposition is evident everywhere in the painting ~ the building at the right with one façade blue and one pink, and the house to the left with grey~blue planks and pink undertones. Even the seemingly haphazard snowflakes are carefully placed and, where needed, change colour so that they can be clearly seen. It is, in short, a work that leaves nothing to chance; Robinson has created a harmonious and satisfying image of a winter long gone and one which was passing even as he captured it in 1928.

ESTIMATE: $100,000 ~ 150,000

28

28 HENRI LEOPOLD MASSON
CGP CSPWC OSA QMG RCA 1907 ~ 1996

Signs of Spring, St~André~Avellin
oil on canvas, on verso titled
22 x 28 in, 55.9 x 71.1 cm

PROVENANCE:
Private Collection, Vancouver

ESTIMATE: $3,500 ~ 4,500

29 ELIZABETH ANNIE MCGILLIVRAY KNOWLES
ARCA 1866 ~ 1928

On the Beaupré Road, Quebec
oil on board, signed and dated 1909 and on verso titled
12 x 10 in, 30.5 x 25.4 cm

ESTIMATE: $6,000 ~ 8,000

30 EDITH GRACE COOMBS
CSGA OSA 1890 ~ 1986

Wylies' Farm, Magnetawan, Ontario
oil on canvas, signed, circa 1933
30 x 40 in, 76.2 x 101.6 cm

PROVENANCE:
Private Collection, Ontario

LITERATURE:
Lorne Pierce, *E. Grace Coombs*, listed in the catalogue raisonné

EXHIBITED:
National Gallery of Canada, Ottawa, 1934

ESTIMATE: $4,000 ~ 5,000

31 LILIAS TORRANCE NEWTON
BHHG CGP RCA 1896 ~ 1980

Portrait of Dyan
oil on canvas, signed
16 x 12 in, 40.6 x 30.5 cm

PROVENANCE:
Private Collection, Montreal

ESTIMATE: $1,200 ~ 1,500

32

32   MAURICE GALBRAITH CULLEN

RCA   1866 ~ 1934

Cape Diamond, Quebec

oil on canvas, signed and on verso titled and certified by
Cullen Inventory #1210, circa 1899
18 1/4 x 29 in, 46.3 x 73.7 cm

PROVENANCE:
Galerie Walter Klinkhoff Inc., Montreal
Private Collection, Ontario, acquired in 1971

LITERATURE:
A.Y. Jackson, *A Painter's Country*, 1958, pages 15 and 16

Cullen, who trained in France at the École Nationale of the Societé des
beaux~arts and the Académie des beaux~arts, was one of the earliest
artists to bring an impressionist palette and technique to the Canadian
landscape. A.Y. Jackson in his autobiography acknowledges Cullen's
effects on his peers, writing that he made them "aware of the fresh and
invigorating movements going on in the art circles of France...To us he
was a hero. His paintings of Quebec City, from Lévis and along the river,
are among the most distinguished works produced in Canada...".

Although he lived much of his life in Montreal, Cullen's city was Quebec.

Again and again he returned to the dramatic site of the city perched above
the St. Lawrence River, views of the city itself and Lévis across the river.
This handsome canvas is a splendid example of Cullen's skills with the
depiction of snow, his use of light and his broken, impressionist
brush~stroke. The use of blue and white within the composition is
extremely successful, shadows being conveyed by greater additions of
blue rather than blacks and thus picking up the colours of both sky and
the intense blue of the water. This allows Cullen to use a pure white to
suggest areas where the landscape is in full sunlight. This was one of those
dazzlingly bright winter days that are still and intensely cold ~ notice the
smoke which rises almost straight up from the chimneys. The intensity of
the light allows Cullen to use brilliant colour in the sun ~ the white of the
snow on the escarpment top and on the river and snow bank on the
opposite side. He has assumed a commanding viewpoint for the painting
and the composition opens out dramatically below the viewer. While we
are aware of the cold and the hardships of living in an at times
inhospitable climate, we are also exhilarated by the grand sweep of the
river, the shimmering light and the sheer exuberance of his paint
application.

ESTIMATE: $100,000 ~ 150,000

33

35

33   PAUL VANIER BEAULIEU
RCA   1910 ~ 1996

Horse and Sleigh in Winter

oil on canvas, signed
18 x 21 1/2 in, 45.7 x 54.6 cm

PROVENANCE:
Private Collection, Montreal
By descent to the present Private Collection, Vancouver

ESTIMATE: $3,000 ~ 4,000

34   RANDOLPH STANLEY HEWTON
BHHG RCA   1888 ~ 1960

Gouffre River in Spring

oil on canvas, signed and on verso stamped with the artist's
studio stamp and stamped with Walter Klinkhoff Gallery
Hewton Estate stamp
20 1/4 x 24 in, 51.4 x 61 cm

PROVENANCE:
Galerie Walter Klinkhoff Inc., Montreal
By descent to the present Private Collection, Toronto

After serving in World War I, Randolph Hewton returned permanently to
his home province of Quebec, settling in Montreal. Hewton often used
natural settings in Quebec as subject matter for his paintings. *Gouffre
River in Spring* is a superb example of Hewton's work, with its graceful
patterns of tree trunks, snow patterns and radiant blue hills.

ESTIMATE: $10,000 ~ 12,000

35   RANDOLPH STANLEY HEWTON
BHHG RCA   1888 ~ 1960

Winter, Quebec Village

oil on canvas, signed, circa 1928
10 x 12 in, 25.4 x 30.5 cm

PROVENANCE:
Private Collection, Toronto

ESTIMATE: $12,000 ~ 15,000

34

36

36   FRANK (FRANZ) HANS JOHNSTON

ARCA CSPWC G7 OSA   1888 ~ 1949

Which Way?

oil on board, signed and on verso titled, circa 1930
22 x 28 in, 55.9 x 71.1 cm

PROVENANCE:
Carroll Fine Arts Limited., Toronto
By descent to the present Private Collection, Toronto

LITERATURE:
Roger Burford Mason, *A Grand Eye for Glory*, 1998, pages 71 and 75

Johnston loved to paint winter scenes, and would paint outdoors even in weather so cold that it would congeal his oil paints. He traveled frequently in the 1930s to the Canadian north, ranging from the Lake Nipigon area in northern Ontario all the way up to Eldorado at Great Bear Lake in the Arctic, painting dog sled scenes in both areas. Mason writes that Johnston "reveled in the brilliance of the light, the intense clarity and colour generated in those rarefied atmospheric conditions." A 1938 exhibition of his northern work brought very favourable reviews from critics: Pearl McCarthy in the *Globe and Mail* praised his "magnificent" colour and his "jewels of light on the snow".

ESTIMATE: $25,000 ~ 35,000

37   FRANK (FRANZ) HANS JOHNSTON
ARCA CSPWC G7 OSA   1888 ~ 1949

Coppermine

oil on board, signed and titled
12 x 16 in, 30.5 x 40.6 cm

PROVENANCE:
Danish Art Gallery, Vancouver

ESTIMATE: $3,000 ~ 4,000

37

38

38   FRANK (FRANZ) HANS JOHNSTON
ARCA CSPWC G7 OSA   1888 ~ 1949

Victory of Spring

oil on board, signed and on verso signed and titled
16 x 20 in, 40.6 x 50.8 cm

PROVENANCE:
Penell Gallery, Toronto
Private Collection, Victoria

ESTIMATE: $15,000 ~ 18,000

39   JAMES FENWICK LANSDOWNE
1937 ~

Great Tit

watercolour on paper, signed and dated 1963 and
on verso titled
17 1/4 x 14 3/4 in, 43.8 x 37.5 cm

PROVENANCE:
The Tryon Gallery Ltd., London
Private Collection, Winnipeg

ESTIMATE: $2,000 ~ 3,000

39

40

40   ALBERT HENRY ROBINSON

ARCA RCA   1881 ~ 1956

Goélettes in the Ice, Baie St. Paul

oil on canvas, signed and dated 1927

27 x 33 in, 68.6 x 83.8 cm

Provenance:

Acquired in 1948 from Watson Art Galleries, Montreal by the present
Private Collection, Ontario

Exhibited:

Art Gallery of Hamilton, Ontario

Robinson traveled to Paris in 1903 to study at the Académie Julian and the
École des Beaux~Arts, where he was influenced by impressionism. A.Y.
Jackson in his autobiography, *A Painter's Country*, mentions that he was
with Robinson in St. Malo and Carhaix in Brittany, where Robinson
painted fishing schooners in the village harbours. Back in Canada,
Jackson relates how in 1924, they spent time together in Baie St. Paul
painting similar subject matter. Robinson sketched with Jackson in
Cacouna, La Malbaie, St. Tite des Caps, Les Eboulements, Bienville and

elsewhere. He also went on sketching trips with other artists such as Clarence Gagnon, Edwin Holgate and Randolph Hewton. Jackson greatly enjoyed his company due to Robinson's warm and amusing nature; an accomplished mimic, Robinson was known to imitate his fellow artists. Jackson also found it interesting that, unlike other artists, Robinson often did not travel far to sketch, but would find his subjects close to where he was staying. Robinson was known to have made painting trips along the St. Lawrence from 1918 to 1933.

This work has Robinson's characteristic bold fresh colour palette brightened by luscious coral, pink and emerald. The downward curve of the wide road in the foreground pulls the viewer's eye straight to the colourful schooners in their bed of ice. Robinson sets up rhythms in the curves of the road, land forms and the ice pan edges. It is a vital composition where each element is strongly defined in a fresh, clear atmosphere.

ESTIMATE: $100,000 ~ 150,000

41a

41   E.J. (EDWARD JOHN) HUGHES
BCSFA RCA 1913 ~

Two Works

a) The Ferry at Crofton, BC
watercolour on paper, signed and dated 1992
and on verso titled and dated
18 x 24 in, 45.7 x 61 cm

b) The Ferry at Crofton, BC
pencil on paper, signed and dated 1963
and on verso signed, titled and dated
10 x 14 in, 25.4 x 35.5 cm

PROVENANCE:
Acquired directly from the Artist by the present Private Collection, Vancouver Island

ESTIMATE: $25,000 ~ 30,000

41b

42

42   FREDERICK HORSMAN VARLEY
ARCA G7 OSA 1881 ~ 1969

Arctic Icebergs
oil on panel, signed (visible under UV light) and artist's
thumbprint and on verso stamped National Gallery of Canada
Varley Inventory #1114, 1938
12 x 15 in, 30.5 x 38.1 cm

PROVENANCE:
The Art Gallery of Toronto, Womens Committee Picture Sale, 1949
By descent to the present Private Collection, Toronto

LITERATURE:
F.H. Varley, A Centennial Exhibition, The Edmonton Art Gallery, 1981,
pages 138 and 140

Frederick Varley, following in the footsteps of A.Y. Jackson and Lawren
Harris, made one trip to the Arctic in 1938. He traveled north on the *RMS
Nascopie* from Montreal and, in the summer of 1938, produced some
striking images of the north. Some of his best sketches are marked by a
remarkable audacity in their form and execution, equal to but quite
distinct from the arctic sketches of Harris. *Arctic Icebergs*, which might
more accurately be described as an icebergscape, is a vivid and splendid
example of Varley at his best. Varley was particularly struck by the
icebergs and wrote to a friend, "the icebergs ~ literally hundreds of them,
floating sphinxes ~ pyramids ~ mountain peaks with castles on them ~
draw~bridges & crevasses, huge cathedrals ~ coral forms magnified a
thousand fold." He was equally struck by the strange colours of the
icebergs, commenting on the "blue greens & the violets" and even the
"mauve & the sea deep purple and red."

ESTIMATE: $60,000 ~ 80,000

43

43   FREDERICK HORSMAN VARLEY

ARCA G7 OSA 1881 ~ 1969

Moonlight, the Trail from Rice Lake

watercolour on paper, signed and on verso titled, dated circa
1935, National Gallery of Canada Varley Inventory #555 and
inscribed *Watercolour painted in Lynn Valley when F.H. Varley
was experimenting with evening and moonlight effects. The figure is
Vera.* Also inscribed *filmed for CBC programme on the Group of
Seven, 14 July 1976*
7 1/2 x 10 in, 19 x 25.4 cm

PROVENANCE:
Acquired directly from the Artist in the 1930s by V. Fount, Vancouver
Gifted to Margaret Williams, Vancouver, circa 1949
Private Collection, Toronto

LITERATURE:
Christopher Varley, *F.H. Varley*, The Edmonton Art Gallery, 1981,
pages 114 ~ 116

EXHIBITED:
Burnaby Art Gallery, *Varley ~ The Middle Years*, May 1 ~ June 2, 1974

Varley was teaching in Vancouver at The British Columbia College of Arts
in the thirties, and by 1934 was living in Lynn Valley in North Vancouver.
Christopher Varley writes: "his house…was nestled on the slope of a hill,
with a panoramic view of Lynn Peak and Mount Seymour…Lynn Creek
itself passed through a deep gorge within one hundred feet of the house,
and was straddled by a bridge that marked the way to Rice Lake, one of
Varley's favourite painting spots." This trail was restored in the nineties
and is now officially called the Varley Trail.

ESTIMATE: $20,000 ~ 25,000

44

44   LAWREN STEWART HARRIS
BCSFA G7 OSA PRCA   1885 ~ 1970

Mountain Sketch, Van Horne Range, XIII (Mountain Sketch XCIV)

oil on panel, signed and on verso signed, titled variously:
Mountain Sketch, Van Horne Range / Mountain Sketch XCIV and
inscribed *XIII / Not for Sale / Reserved*, circa 1928
12 x 15 in, 30.5 x 38.1 cm

PROVENANCE:
Dominion Gallery, Montreal; Private Collection, Toronto

Lawren Harris first visited the Rockies in 1924 and was, at least initially,
unimpressed. He was soon won over by the grandeur of the mountain
landscape and came to regard this region of the country as a vital wellspring
of his art. He returned many times and produced an important body of
drawings and sketches. This work, which interestingly has both a title that
specifies a location and a more generic *Mountain Sketch* number, is typical of
the many images that come from the later years of the twenties as he began to
move increasingly towards abstraction. The distant peaks, here separated
from the viewer by a series of lower mountains, represented for Harris the
spiritual realm to which all enlightened people aspired. The journey that we
make is an intellectual and emotional one rather than a physical one and
this purer existence is suggested by the use of blue (a colour of spiritual
awareness in his beliefs) and the use of generalized form rather than specific
detail. This general sense of a spiritual journey, which one might make in
this northern landscape, was complimented by the more generic titles that
Harris initially employed. This strategy was undermined by the more
everyday~minded of his viewers who soon asked which mountain or
mountain range it was, leading no doubt to the use of the more specific title
of *Van Horne Range*. Harris's treatment of the Rocky Mountains, in his
sketches and the canvases they inspired, are amongst the most distinctive
and important contributions that Harris made to Canadian art.

ESTIMATE: $100,000 ~ 150,000

45

45   LAWREN STEWART HARRIS
BCSFA G7 OSA PRCA 1885 ~ 1970

Wenchemna Lake, Rocky Mountains
(Mountain Sketch XCV)

oil on panel, on verso signed twice, titled variously: *Near Wenchemna Lake, Rocky Mts / Mountain Sketch / Wenchemna Lake / Mountain Sketch XCV* and inscribed *not for sale*, circa 1927
12 x 15 in, 30.5 x 38.1 cm

PROVENANCE:
Private Collection, Vancouver

LITERATURE:
Peter Larisey, *Light for a Cold Land, Lawren Harris's Work and Life ~ An Interpretation*, 1993, page 100

Harris made the first of several trips to the Rockies in 1924. He returned every year until 1929. The experience of working in the Rockies was to result in some of Harris's most memorable canvases and he produced a highly accomplished group of sketches and drawings as well. As most writers on Harris have commented, the Rockies seemed to provide subject matter which allowed him to explore the spiritual side of his Theosophical beliefs. Peter Larisey writes: "Harris's response to the mountains was deeply emotional." B.C. Binning accompanied Harris on mountain climbing expeditions. "Binning remembers that, after one long and arduous climb, Harris was deeply moved when he finally reached the peak: in a trancelike state, he experienced glossalalia, and began an ecstatic, unintelligible chanting." The simple, majestic forms of the mountains, devoid of human presence, a cool palette and the use of revelatory light are found in all of Harris's best Rocky Mountain sketches ~ of which this painting is one.

ESTIMATE: $100,000 ~ 150,000

46   LAWREN STEWART HARRIS

BCSFA G7 OSA PRCA   1885 ~ 1970

Abstraction 119

oil on canvas, on verso stamped
Lawren Harris LSH Holdings 119, circa 1945
57 1/2 x 47 1/4 in, 146 x 120 cm

PROVENANCE:
Stewart Wallace, Vancouver
Kenneth G. Heffel Fine Art Inc., Vancouver
Loch & Mayberry Fine Art Inc., Winnipeg
Private Collection, Winnipeg

LITERATURE:
Lawren Harris, Retrospective Exhibition, National Gallery of Canada and
the Vancouver Art Gallery, 1963, catalogue #52
Peter Larisey, *Light for a Cold Land, Lawren Harris's Work and Life ~ An
Interpretation*, 1993, reproduced plate 45, page 163

EXHIBITED:
The Art Gallery of Toronto, *Lawren Harris*, October ~ November 1948,
catalogue #64, label on verso
National Gallery of Canada, Ottawa and the Vancouver Art Gallery,
Lawren Harris, Retrospective Exhibition, 1963, catalogue #52, label on
verso

Harris began to move towards abstraction in his paintings of the later
twenties and by the late thirties was producing almost exclusively
abstract works. His association with the transcendental painters in New
Mexico heightened this interest in abstraction. Nevertheless, decades of
painting the landscape had left its mark on Harris and in a number of
important paintings elements of landscape and abstraction merge. As
Peter Larisey has noted, *Abstraction 119* "gathers together Harris's interest
in abstract triangles and other geometric forms, selected natural forms,
and tiny, well~contained landscape views similar to his Lake Superior
works." Natural clouds emerge from geometric spaces and there is an
interrupted landscape in the lower section of the work. Larisey has
suggested that "Harris probably thought of the work as a fusion of natural
and abstract forms that embodied the contribution each can make to
spiritual expression." The success of the painting rests on the lively
tension between the abstract and landscape elements. It is interesting to
speculate on the effect that such a work would have had in the relatively
conservative art world of Vancouver at the end of the war. It is a
challenging and provocative attempt to meld the physical with the
spiritual world. The use of colour and dynamic linear pattern, organic
and geometric shapes and a diffuse, unreal light source all contribute to
the sense of mystery and ambiguity in the work. It is of the world and yet
unworldly and, in the end, seems to evoke perfectly Harris's belief in the
"everlasting divine spirit."

This is without question the finest Harris abstract painting that we have
had the pleasure to offer at auction.

ESTIMATE: $70,000 ~ 90,000

47

47   LAWREN STEWART HARRIS

BCSFA G7 OSA PRCA   1885 ~ 1970

LSH 128

oil on board, signed and on verso
signed, titled and dated 1958
30 1/4 x 24 in, 76.8 x 61 cm

PROVENANCE:
Estate of the Artist

LITERATURE:
Dennis Reid, *Atma Buddhi Manas: The Later Work of Lawren S. Harris*, Art
Gallery of Ontario, 1985, page 56, the larger version of this work
reproduced page 98, catalogue #75
Bess Harris and R.G.P. Colgrove, *Lawren Harris*, 1969, the larger version
of this work reproduced page 129

The early part of 1958 found Harris in a surge of inventive work. Harris's
abstract work was a creative revolution, a visionary reflection of his
profound spiritual beliefs. Dennis Reid writes that the work of the fifties
"had introduced a somewhat more atmospheric space, and as we noted
earlier, a more highly developed sense of colour…The sense of palpable
light is almost hypnotic."

ESTIMATE: $10,000 ~ 12,000

48

48   FREDERICK HORSMAN VARLEY

ARCA G7 OSA   1881 ~ 1969

Kootenay Lake

oil on canvas, signed and artist's thumbprint, circa 1958
24 x 30 in, 61 x 76.2 cm

PROVENANCE:
By descent to the present Private Collection, Toronto

LITERATURE:
Christopher Varley, *F.H. Varley*, The Edmonton Art Gallery, 1981,
reproduced page 173, incorrectly captioned

EXHIBITED:
The Edmonton Art Gallery, *F.H. Varley: A Centennial Exhibition*, 1981,
traveling to the Art Gallery of Greater Victoria; National Gallery of Canada,
Ottawa; the Montreal Museum of Fine Arts and the Art Gallery of Ontario,
Toronto, 1982

Although Varley did not live in British Columbia again after leaving in
1936, he retained a great fondness for the province and made a number of
summer painting trips to BC between 1957 and 1967. The landscape
which seemed particularly to appeal to him during this latter part of his
life was the Kootenay Lake region, and there are a number of drawings
and paintings of the area. This is one of the relatively few larger canvases
depicting this part of British Columbia. Varley's fondness for blues and

greens remained, and this unusual colour palette gives works such as *Kootenay Lake* a deeply spiritual feeling. The artist's grandson, Christopher, has linked the use of shafts of sunlight in many of these works to Varley's interest in the work of the great nineteenth century British painter Joseph M.W. Turner. It is certainly true that Varley found the landscape of British Columbia ~ which he initially felt only early Chinese painters could do justice to ~ a source of ongoing and deep inspiration. This canvas has a sense of revelation which is enhanced by the shaft of light that illuminates the water and also by the aureoles that appear at the edges of the clouds and the lack of specificity of the topography. This is not simply a portrait of a piece of the landscape but rather an invitation for the viewer to travel to the spiritual realm that Varley admired. The painting is more about the spirit, the mystery of the place, than the specifics of the landscape.

ESTIMATE: $80,000 ~ 120,000

49

49   FRANK (FRANZ) HANS JOHNSTON
ARCA CSPWC G7 OSA   1888 ~ 1949

Near Parry Sound, Rankin Lake
oil on canvas on panel, signed and on verso titled and inscribed *I certify this sketch to be an authentic work by my father Franz Johnston ~ Paul Rodrik*
7 x 9 in, 17.8 x 22.9 cm

PROVENANCE:
Private Collection, Ontario

ESTIMATE: $6,000 ~ 8,000

50

50   WILLIAM GOODRIDGE ROBERTS
OSA RCA   1904 ~ 1974

Laurentians
oil on board, signed
24 x 36 in, 61 x 91.4 cm

PROVENANCE:
By descent to the present Private Collection, Toronto

ESTIMATE: $10,000 ~ 15,000

51   W.P. (WILLIAM PERCIVAL) WESTON
ARCA BCSFA CGP   1879 ~ 1967

Atlin, BC
oil on canvas, signed and on verso signed, titled and dated 1956
27 1/4 x 32 in, 69.2 x 81.3 cm

PROVENANCE:
Private Collection, Toronto

ESTIMATE: $10,000 ~ 15,000

51

52

52   FRANKLIN CARMICHAEL
G7 OSA RCA 1890 ~ 1945

Port Coldwell Bay, North Shore, Lake Superior
watercolour on paper, signed and dated 1928 and on verso
signed, titled and inscribed on a label in the artist's hand: *11
Cameron Ave, Lansing, Ontario; 1930 Group of Seven, Toronto;
1930 Group of Seven, Montreal; 1931 Hartt* [sic] *House, Toronto*
17 1/4 x 21 1/4 in, 43.8 x 54 cm

PROVENANCE:
By descent to the present Private Collection, Toronto

LITERATURE:
Canadian Painting and Sculpture, Canadian National Exhibition, 1932,
reproduced catalogue #468
Jeremy Adamson, *Lawren S. Harris*, Art Gallery of Ontario, 1978, for a
painting of the same scene entitled *Lake Superior III* by Lawren Harris, in
the collection of the National Gallery of Canada, reproduced page 160
Megan Bice, *Light & Shadow, The Work of Franklin Carmichael*, McMichael
Canadian Art Collection, 1990, for a Carmichael painting entitled *North
Shore, Lake Superior* in the collection of the Montreal Museum of Fine
Arts, reproduced page 42

EXHIBITED:
Art Gallery of Toronto, *Exhibition of the Group of Seven*, April 5 ~ 27, 1930,
catalogue #17
Art Association of Montreal, *Exhibition of Paintings and Drawings by the
Group of Seven and by Other Artists Invited by Them to Contribute*, May 3 ~
18, 1930, catalogue #17
Canadian National Exhibition, Toronto, *Canadian Painting and Sculpture*,
August 22 ~ September 6, 1930, catalogue #347
National Gallery of Canada, Ottawa, *Annual Exhibition of Canadian Art*,
January 15 ~ February 28, 1931, with the title *Port Coldwell Bay* on the
exhibition label, catalogue #36
Hart House, Toronto, 1931
National Gallery of Canada, Ottawa, *Seventh Annual Exhibition of
Canadian Art*, January 22 ~ February 23, 1932, titled *Port Coldwell Bay* on
the label on verso
Canadian National Exhibition, Toronto, *Canadian Painting and Sculpture*,
August 26 ~ September 6, 1932, reproduced in the catalogue, #468, titled
Coldwell Bay, N.S. Lake Superior on the label on verso
Royal Scottish Academy Galleries, Edinburgh, *Royal Scottish Society of
Painters in Watercolour*, January 27 ~ March 4, 1933, catalogue #260,
valued at 40 pounds on the National Gallery of Canada label

Of all the members of the Group of Seven it was the two youngest,
Franklin Carmichael and his protégé, A.J. Casson, who were most
interested in watercolour. For both men, watercolour was an important
sketching medium and large~scale watercolours such as this one were of
significant importance in their careers. In the use of these large~scale
works, Carmichael recalls the watercolour work of artists such as Lucius
O'Brien from the nineteenth century. The importance of watercolour for
Carmichael (and Casson) is evident in the crucial role that both men
played in founding the Canadian Society of Painters in Watercolour in
1926. In the 1930 Group exhibition a room was devoted to their
watercolours and *Port Coldwell Bay, North Shore, Lake Superior* was
included in this exhibition. Carmichael felt that larger scale watercolours
could capture the drama and power of the landscape as well as oil painting
could. His belief in the success of this watercolour is illustrated by its
extensive exhibiting history in the early 1930s.

Port Coldwell Bay, North Shore, Lake Superior is the product of one of his
sketching trips to the north shore of Lake Superior. Executed in the
studio, it is an image of dynamic movement and portrays a vista of
sweeping grandeur. It recalls the imagery of Lawren Harris but has the
greater delicacy of the watercolour medium and is, perhaps, not as austere
as some of Harris's images. What is certainly clear in this image is
Carmichael's absolute command of the watercolour medium and his
enormous skill in creating an effective and exciting composition.

The foreground group of stark trees stands before a sweeping landscape
that can only be described as majestic. The physical beauty of the
landscape was of paramount importance to Carmichael and he captures it
through the judicious use of dark and light areas ~ light in the immediate
foreground, dark in the near hills to suggest the falling away of the land,
light on the expanse of Lake Superior and then dark again in the distant
hills. The elegant curve of the dead trees in the foreground contrasts with
the v~shaped forms on the water and the rolling hills in both fore~ and
background. The stillness of the landscape is counteracted by the sense of
movement in both the water and the clouds in the windswept sky. What is
particularly remarkable about this work is Carmichael's use of colour ~ it
is a veritable symphony of blue. The control of this single colour,
combined with touches of grey and yellow, give the image a richness and
subtlety that suggests just how skilled he was with this most difficult
medium. Watercolour is not forgiving of mistakes, but here it is handled
with confidence and assurance. The composition is deliberately and
carefully built up but there is no sense of this labour, simply a belief in the
power of the image and the beauty of the landscape. Carmichael has given
us the experience of Port Coldwell through the strength of his vision.

ESTIMATE: $80,000 ~ 120,000

53

53 ARTHUR LISMER
CSPWC G7 OSA RCA 1885 ~ 1969

On Pender Island, East Coast of Vancouver Island, BC

oil on board, signed and dated 1951 and on verso signed, titled and dated
16 x 20 in, 40.6 x 50.8 cm

PROVENANCE:
Acquired directly from the Artist by John Bland, the Dean of Architecture at McGill University, Montreal as a wedding gift in 1951 to the present Private Collection, Vancouver

LITERATURE:
Lois Darroch, *Bright Land,* 1981, page 151

In 1951 Lismer traveled to Long Beach on Vancouver Island and also explored Pender and Galiano Islands. He returned to Vancouver Island every summer thereafter for sixteen years. The change of landscape brought a fresh vision to Lismer. He was struck by the power of the great forests and the light, which was so different from the east. He knew Emily Carr, and had even sketched with her in Victoria on an earlier trip, and although his depiction of nature was not as mystical, he was certainly aware of the life force present in the coastal forest. Darroch writes about the BC work that "Lismer's paintings were nevertheless filled with the earth force, the vitality that was undeniably his mark. The colours of his palette were more restricted. Green predominated, for he was surrounded by the lush vegetation of the forest, and growth was the essence of the life Lismer loved."

ESTIMATE: $30,000 ~ 40,000

54

56

54   A.Y. (ALEXANDER YOUNG) JACKSON

CGP G7 OSA RCA RSA   1882 ~ 1974

Near Go Home Bay

oil on panel, signed
10 1/2 x 13 1/2 in, 26.7 x 34.3 cm

PROVENANCE:

By descent to the present Private Collection, Barrie, Ontario

LITERATURE:

A.Y. Jackson, *A Painter's Country*, 1958, pages 25 and 74

Jackson first traveled to Go Home Bay in Georgian Bay in 1913 when Dr. MacCallum, a patron of the Group of Seven, offered him the use of his comfortable house on an island there to paint. There, Jackson writes, "Paddling around islands and exploring intricate channels and bays that cut into the mainland provided me with much material." He was there again in 1922, and wrote that "Go Home Bay and the outer islands are filled for me with happy memories of good friends and of efforts...that I made to portray its ever~varying moods."

ESTIMATE: $12,000 ~ 16,000

55   FREDERICK STANLEY HAINES

OSA PRCA   1879 ~ 1960

Chinese Island

oil on canvas on board, signed and on verso titled, circa 1930
10 x 12 in, 25.4 x 30.5 cm

ESTIMATE: $2,500 ~ 3,000

56   ARTHUR LISMER

CSPWC G7 OSA RCA   1885 ~ 1969

Georgian Bay, Pines and Rocks

oil on board, signed and dated 1950
12 x 16 in, 30.5 x 40.6 cm

LITERATURE:

Lois Darroch, *Bright Land*, 1981, page 15

Lismer's fondness for Georgian Bay goes back to his first visit in 1920, and he continued to return to it. Darroch writes: "It is like being on a different continent ~ the radiant air, the rocks, the endless expanse of turbulent water and sky, the magnificent sturdy stance of pine trees pitted against the wind...It was a Canada Lismer never dreamed could exist. He was shaken by the revelation of the new and wonderful landscape."

ESTIMATE: $10,000 ~ 15,000

57

57 WILLIAM KURELEK

OSA RCA 1927 ~ 1977

Near Dawson Creek

mixed media on board, on verso titled, 1973
47 1/2 x 48 3/4 in, 120.6 x 123.8 cm

PROVENANCE:

Isaacs Gallery, Toronto; Anglo Canadian Pulp & Paper Company
Private Collection, Toronto

EXHIBITED:

Burnaby Art Gallery, *A Prairie Painter in the Mountains*, 1973

During Kurelek's lifetime he painted Canada from coast to coast. His
childhood on the prairies on farms in Alberta and Manitoba gave him a

love and awe for the expansiveness of skies and horizons and the power of the forces of nature over the land. He most often depicts people or their habitations as small in a large landscape, as with this finely detailed farm scene. Kurelek was very religious, which imbued his work with a sense of a mystical union with nature. Certainly that feeling is present in this idyllic panorama with its glorious sky and heightened, almost surreal, green. Kurelek captured the essence of Canada's vast beauty.

This work is accompanied by a letter from the Isaacs Gallery stating the history of the painting.

ESTIMATE: $25,000 ~ 35,000

59

59 CLAYTON ANDERSON
1964 ~

Mermaid Cove
acrylic on board, signed and dated 2005
and on verso signed, titled and dated
37 1/2 x 29 3/4 in, 95.2 x 75.6 cm

Clayton Anderson was born in Vancouver, BC in 1964. He was trained as a graphic designer at the Alberta College of Art, graduating in 1988 with a diploma in Visual Arts. After working in the advertising art department of *Western Living* and *Vancouver Living* magazines, he turned to painting full~time in 1991. Anderson lives on BC's Sunshine Coast with his wife and daughter, and this work is a beautiful example of the artist's treatment of the soft, diffuse light of his environment.

ESTIMATE: $4,000 ~ 6,000

58

58 WILLIAM KURELEK
OSA RCA 1927 ~ 1977

Uranium Mines at Quirke Lake
mixed media on board, signed and dated 1970
19 x 14 3/4 in, 48.3 x 37.5 cm

PROVENANCE:
Isaacs Gallery, Toronto; Private Collection, Toronto

ESTIMATE: $10,000 ~ 15,000

60

60   LAWREN STEWART HARRIS

BCSFA G7 OSA PRCA 1885 ~ 1970

Northern Lake

oil on panel, signed and on verso signed, titled and inscribed
Bess Harris Collection, property of Bess Harris, circa 1920 ~ 1925
10 1/2 x 14 1/2 in, 26.7 x 36.8 cm

PROVENANCE:
Estate of the Artist
Private Collection, Ontario

Harris and his colleagues in the Group of Seven dramatically changed landscape painting in Canada. This was not because they painted areas never before painted but because of the character of their approach. Harris in particular developed a style that suggested a landscape that was removed from human experience. There is, of course, the fact that he observed the landscape, but there is a desolate quality in much of his

painting that suggests that these landscapes are not hospitable ones. The sheer emptiness of the landscape was something that appealed to Harris as an artist and allowed him to explore his interest in colour and design. *Northern Lake* was likely done in the early to mid~twenties on one of the sketching trips that Harris took with Jackson and others to the northern shore of Lake Superior. The panel is a delicate balance of blues and oranges, something quite unlike what Harris actually saw ~ but a portrait of the landscape was of less interest to Harris than his ability to convey the essence of his experience of it. The vastness of the landscape is conveyed, despite the modest scale of the panel, through the use of light and shadow and the overlapping planes of the landforms. The blue that touches the mountaintops suggests a great distance, and the whole scene is viewed from an elevated situation. Harris was interested in the simple majesty of nature and how that nature might lead us to a more spiritual life. We are here freed of any distractions from the purity of Harris's vision, and there is no narrative beyond what we might ourselves provide. For Harris the purity of this northern landscape was important in and of itself, particularly since it might lead those who contemplate it to a higher level of spiritual understanding.

ESTIMATE: $90,000 ~ 120,000

62

61

61 LAWREN STEWART HARRIS
BCSFA G7 OSA PRCA 1885 ~ 1970

Rocky Mountain Drawing 9 ~ 36

graphite on paper, on verso inscribed
Book 9 ~ 36, circa 1924 ~ 1930
8 x 10 in, 20.3 x 25.4 cm

PROVENANCE:
Estate of Lawren Stewart Harris
Estate of Howard K. Harris

LITERATURE:
Catherine Mastin, *The Group of Seven in Western Canada*, Glenbow Museum, 2002, listed on page 199

EXHIBITED:
Glenbow Museum, Calgary, *The Group of Seven in Western Canada*, 2002, traveling to the Art Gallery of Nova Scotia, Halifax, Winnipeg Art Gallery, Art Gallery of Greater Victoria and the National Gallery of Canada, Ottawa, 2003 ~ 2004, catalogue #44

ESTIMATE: $3,500 ~ 4,500

62 LAWREN STEWART HARRIS
BCSFA G7 OSA PRCA 1885 ~ 1970

Algonquin #1, South Tea Lake

pencil on paper, inscribed with the artist's size notations in pencil, circa 1920
5 3/4 x 7 in, 14.6 x 17.8 cm

PROVENANCE:
Manuge Galleries, Halifax
Yaneff International Gallery, Toronto
Private Collection, Toronto

LITERATURE:
Charles C. Hill, *The Group of Seven*, 1995, a related oil painting reproduced on page 103 and on the front cover of the book

There are three large oil paintings related to this drawing: *North Painting XXV*, *Northern Island*, and *Island ~ MacCallum Lake* which is reproduced on the cover of the Group of Seven book. Interestingly, Group of Seven artists gave the names of friends to unnamed sites; MacCallum Lake is a made~up name and this drawing may shed light on the correct location of *Algonquin #1, South Tea Lake*.

The artist has produced this very fine drawing on two overlapping pieces of paper which he then adhered with paper tape in order to preserve the entire drawing. This is confirmed by two size notations in the upper margin (6 3/4) and left~hand margin (5 3/4) indicating Harris's final choice of outer border markings.

ESTIMATE: $6,000 ~ 8,000

63

66

64

67

65

68

63 LAWREN STEWART HARRIS
BCSFA G7 OSA PRCA 1885 ~ 1970

Rocky Mountain Drawing 9 ~ 42
graphite on paper, on verso inscribed
Book 9 ~ 42, circa 1924 ~ 1930
8 x 10 in, 20.3 x 25.4 cm

PROVENANCE:
Estate of Lawren Stewart Harris; Estate of Howard K. Harris

LITERATURE:
Catherine Mastin, *The Group of Seven in Western Canada*, Glenbow
Museum, 2002, listed on page 199

EXHIBITED:
Glenbow Museum, Calgary, *The Group of Seven in Western Canada*, 2002,
traveling to the Art Gallery of Nova Scotia, Halifax, Winnipeg Art Gallery,
Art Gallery of Greater Victoria and the National Gallery of Canada,
Ottawa, 2003 ~ 2004, catalogue #44

ESTIMATE: $3,500 ~ 4,500

64 CLARENCE ALPHONSE GAGNON
RCA 1881 ~ 1942

Canton de Glaris, Vallée du Linthal, Switzerland
oil on panel, on verso certified by Lucile Rodier Gagnon
and artist's thumbprint twice, 1926
6 1/4 x 9 in, 15.9 x 22.9 cm

PROVENANCE:
Loch Art Gallery, Winnipeg; Private Collection, Toronto

Gagnon had deep connections to France, and traveled throughout Europe.
He first arrived in Paris in 1904 to attend the Académie Julian. He traveled
between Quebec and France frequently, and eventually settled in Paris in
1924 for twelve years while he worked on his famous illustrations for the
books *Le Grand Silence Blanc* and *Maria Chapdelaine*. In 1926 he went on
holiday to Switzerland, where this dramatic mountain scene was painted.

ESTIMATE: $7,500 ~ 9,500

65 LAWREN STEWART HARRIS
BCSFA G7 OSA PRCA 1885 ~ 1970

Rocky Mountain Drawing 9 ~ 11
graphite on paper, on verso inscribed
Book 9 ~ 11, circa 1924 ~ 1930
8 x 10 in, 20.3 x 25.4 cm

PROVENANCE:
Estate of Lawren Stewart Harris; Estate of Howard K. Harris

LITERATURE:
Catherine Mastin, *The Group of Seven in Western Canada*, Glenbow
Museum, 2002, listed on page 199

EXHIBITED:
Glenbow Museum, Calgary, *The Group of Seven in Western Canada*, 2002,
traveling to the Art Gallery of Nova Scotia, Halifax, Winnipeg Art Gallery,
Art Gallery of Greater Victoria and the National Gallery of Canada,
Ottawa, 2003 ~ 2004, catalogue #44

ESTIMATE: $3,500 ~ 4,500

66 SIR FREDERICK GRANT BANTING
1891 ~ 1941

Trees in Autumn
oil on panel, circa 1930
10 1/2 x 13 1/2 in, 26.7 x 34.3 cm

PROVENANCE:
Lady Henrietta Banting, Toronto
By descent to the present Private Collection, Toronto

ESTIMATE: $8,000 ~ 10,000

67 A.Y. (ALEXANDER YOUNG) JACKSON
CGP G7 OSA RCA RSA 1882 ~ 1974

Oak Trees, Combermere
oil on panel, signed and on verso
signed, titled and dated October 1960
10 1/2 x 13 1/2 in, 26.7 x 34.3 cm

PROVENANCE:
Private Collection, Vancouver

ESTIMATE: $10,000 ~ 12,000

68 HENRIETTA MABEL MAY
ARCA BHHG CGP RPS 1884 ~ 1971

Autumn Lake
oil on board, signed, circa 1930
18 x 22 in, 45.7 x 55.9 cm

PROVENANCE:
Estate of the Artist; Private Collection, Vancouver

Mabel May first studied in Montreal with William Brymner, later traveling
to France where she was influenced by the work of the impressionists.
When she returned to Canada, she became part of a thriving community
of women artists in Montreal including Prudence Heward, Sarah
Robertson, Lilias Torrance Newton and Kathleen Morris, who banded
together to share studio space, and worked together as the Beaver Hall
Group. Mabel May painted with A.Y. Jackson, Edwin Holgate and
Clarence Gagnon at Baie St. Paul in 1924, and she contributed work to the
Group of Seven's exhibition in 1928 in Toronto.

There is an unfinished portrait on verso.

ESTIMATE: $6,000 ~ 8,000

69

69   A.Y. (ALEXANDER YOUNG) JACKSON
CGP G7 OSA RCA RSA 1882 ~ 1974

Algoma
oil on panel, signed and on verso
signed, titled and dated 1919
8 1/2 x 10 1/2 in, 21.6 x 26.7 cm

PROVENANCE:
Roberts Gallery, Toronto
By descent to the present Private Collection, Toronto

LITERATURE:
A.Y. Jackson, *A Painter's Country*, 1958, page 46, similar work reproduced page 47

After returning to Canada at the end of World War I, Jackson went on the first of his numerous trips to Algoma, a vast landscape stretching from south of Sudbury to the west to the region above Sault Ste. Marie. In the autumn of 1919, Lawren Harris organized the second of the famous boxcar trips to this area with Jackson, J.E.H. MacDonald and Frank Johnston. The boxcar was outfitted with bunks, a stove and canoe and was moved by hand using a three~wheel jigger. By day they painted and by night they gathered around the stove in the boxcar for philosophical and artistic discussions and arguments. Jackson considered this area, with its panorama of long rolling hills, woods and lakes to be "opulent", with "a sublime order to it". This painting, with its rich reds and yellows and its perspective from the midst of the rolling layers of rocks, gives the warm feeling of being enfolded by the land. Throughout his life, Jackson's paintings conveyed his passion for the land and its rhythms, and this work is a very fine example of that passion.

ESTIMATE: $20,000 ~ 25,000

70

70   A.Y. (ALEXANDER YOUNG) JACKSON
CGP G7 OSA RCA RSA   1882 ~ 1974

Algoma
oil on panel, signed, circa 1919
8 1/2 x 10 1/2 in, 21.6 x 26.7 cm

PROVENANCE:
Private Collection, Montreal

LITERATURE:
Naomi Jackson Groves, *A.Y.'s Canada*, 1968, page 114
A.Y. Jackson, *A Painter's Country*, 1958, page 46

Algoma was one of Jackson's favourite parts of Canada, and even though it was a large area stretching from south of Sudbury and westward to above Sault St. Marie, he explored much of it. Groves writes, "This country, with

its vast receding stretches of long~rolling forms, is the type that J.E.H. MacDonald and A.Y. have both loved to tackle." The second boxcar trip taken into this country in 1919 with Jackson, Lawren Harris, J.E.H. MacDonald and Frank Johnston, thrilled them with its beauty. Jackson wrote: "Outside, the aurora played antics in the sky, and the murmur of the rapids or a distant waterfall blended with the silence of the night." Their boxcar would be moved every few days, and they immersed themselves in each new view of the country. Jackson anchors the painting with the strong foreground rock formations, then pulls the eye to the expansive vista on the horizon. This sketch is a superb example of Jackson's skills as a colourist with its intense blue sky and bright slashes of orange~red autumn leaves, which give a feeling of warmth and gaiety to the magnificent solitude.

ESTIMATE: $20,000 ~ 25,000

71

73

72

74

71   FREDERIC MARLETT BELL~SMITH

OSA RCA 1846 ~ 1923

Returning Home

watercolour on paper, signed and dated 1887
13 3/4 x 20 1/2 in, 34.9 x 52.1 cm

PROVENANCE:
Private Collection, Ontario

ESTIMATE: $1,500 ~ 2,000

72   FREDERICK ARTHUR VERNER

ARCA OSA 1836 ~ 1928

Village with Thatched Roof Cottages

watercolour on paper, signed and dated 1885
11 3/4 x 23 in, 29.8 x 58.4 cm

PROVENANCE:
Private Collection, Toronto

ESTIMATE: $1,500 ~ 2,000

73   FREDERICK ARTHUR VERNER

ARCA OSA 1836 ~ 1928

Evening Star

watercolour on paper, signed and dated 1884
13 3/4 x 20 in, 34.9 x 50.8 cm

PROVENANCE:
Private Collection, Ontario

ESTIMATE: $5,000 ~ 7,000

74   PAUL PEEL

OSA RCA 1860 ~ 1892

Young Girl on a Hilltop

oil on canvas, signed and dated 1883
15 1/4 x 25 1/2 in, 38.7 x 64.8 cm

ESTIMATE: $20,000 ~ 25,000

75

77

75   JOHN KASYN

CSPWC OSA 1926 ~

Behind Maclaren & Percy St., Ottawa

oil and lucite on board, signed and dated
1974 and on verso signed, titled and dated
20 x 16 in, 50.8 x 40.6 cm

PROVENANCE:
Private Collection, Toronto

ESTIMATE: $5,000 ~ 7,000

76   JOHN KASYN

CSPWC OSA 1926 ~

Morning Shadows on Seaton Lane, Toronto

oil on board, signed and dated 1978
and on verso signed, titled and dated
14 x 18 in, 35.6 x 45.7 cm

ESTIMATE: $6,000 ~ 8,000

77   ALBERT JACQUES FRANCK

ARCA CSPWC OSA 1899 ~ 1973

Back of Ontario Street

oil on board, signed and dated 1972
and on verso titled on label
16 x 12 in, 40.6 x 30.5 cm

ESTIMATE: $7,000 ~ 8,000

76

78

81

79

82

80

83

78 **JACK LEONARD SHADBOLT**
BCSFA CGP RCA 1909 ~ 1998

Under the Awnings, Granville Street,
Vancouver (Watercolour Sketch for United
Services Centre Mural Panel)

watercolour on paper, signed and dated 1943
and on verso signed, titled and dated
14 1/2 x 22 in, 36.8 x 55.9 cm

PROVENANCE:
Private Collection, Ontario

LITERATURE:
Scott Watson, *Jack Shadbolt*, 1990, page 32

In the summer of 1943, Jack Shadbolt began a large mural for the United Services Recreation Centre depicting a comprehensive view of Vancouver in wartime that was meant to be, as noted by Scott Watson, "topical and documentary ~ an epic in civilian outfits and military uniforms". The architectural detail was exact and specific, with the advertising for the Granville Street merchants clearly illustrated.

This work is one of the rare surviving watercolour sketches for the mural, which no longer exists.

ESTIMATE: $18,000 ~ 22,000

79 **WILLIAM ARTHUR WINTER**
OSA RCA 1909 ~ 1996

Boys with Gliders

oil on artist board, signed and on verso titled
18 x 24 in, 45.7 x 61 cm

PROVENANCE:
Roberts Gallery, Toronto
By descent to the present Private Collection, Toronto

ESTIMATE: $3,000 ~ 4,000

80 **SERGE BRUNONI**
1938 ~

Montreal, le Promenade Devant le Ritz

acrylic on canvas, signed and on verso signed and titled
30 x 40 in, 76.2 x 101.6 cm

ESTIMATE: $2,500 ~ 3,500

81 **WILLIAM ARTHUR WINTER**
OSA RCA 1909 ~ 1996

Children Skipping

oil on board, signed
19 x 31 1/2 in, 48.3 x 80 cm

PROVENANCE:
By descent to the present Private Collection, Toronto

ESTIMATE: $3,500 ~ 4,500

82 **JOHN GEOFFREY CARUTHERS LITTLE**
ARCA 1928 ~

Rue St~Christophe, une Journée Humide
de Mars, Montreal

oil on canvas, signed and on verso signed, titled, dated 1980
and inscribed *Rue St. Christophe was named after Isaac*
Christophe who owned the land in 1845 and Épicere Vincelette,
Académie Le Moyne
24 x 30 in, 61 x 76.2 cm

PROVENANCE:
La Galerie Continentale, Montreal
Private Collection, Quebec

ESTIMATE: $10,000 ~ 15,000

83 **TERRY TOMALTY**
1935 ~

St. Henri

oil on canvas, signed and on verso signed and titled
24 x 30 in, 61 x 76.2 cm

PROVENANCE:
Private Collection, Montreal

ESTIMATE: $3,000 ~ 4,000

84

84   EMILY CARR
BCSFA RCA 1871 ~ 1945

Town in Brittany
oil on canvas, signed, 1911
13 x 16 in, 33 x 40.6 cm

PROVENANCE:
Continental Galleries, Montreal, 1960
Private Collection, Ontario

Emily Carr's brief period of study in France was concentrated in the year
1911 when she worked with several teachers ~ notably the British
expatriates John Duncan Fergusson and Phelan Gibb. It was particularly
in her work with the latter artist at Crécy~en~Brie and later in St. Efflam in
Brittany that Carr developed the vocabulary of bright, post~impressionist
colour and an approach to landscape that was to serve her well upon her
return to Canada. As was the case when she had studied in Cornwall years
before, Carr worked out~of~doors, but now, thanks to a freeing of her
colour palette from naturalism, she was able to express herself more
brilliantly. The handling of colour, light and the paint itself, achieves a
new freedom in these works and established Carr as an artist of
consequence. While in France, Carr depicted the villages she worked in
and the surrounding landscape. She seems to have been particularly
interested in the architecture of the French countryside, and several
cottages appear in paintings from this period. The work expresses Carr's
new confidence as a painter, and it is this confidence that allowed her to
return to Canada and produce the brilliant 1912 canvases of First Nations
subject matter.

ESTIMATE: $70,000 ~ 90,000

85

85   BESS LARKIN HOUSSER HARRIS
BCSFA   RCA   1890 ~ 1969

Old Mine Shaft, Cobalt
oil on canvas, signed and on verso signed, circa 1930
32 x 40 in, 81.3 x 101.6 cm

EXHIBITED:

Art Gallery of Toronto, *The Group of Seven*, December 4 ~ 24, 1931,
catalogue #81

International Art Centre of Roerich Museum, New York, 1932, catalogue #25

Bess Housser Harris, although mostly self~taught, took lessons from F.H.
Varley. In 1914 she married Fred B. Housser, the author of *A Canadian Art
Movement: The Story of the Group of Seven*. Bess wrote about art and edited for
the *Canadian Bookman* from 1923 ~ 1926, and being an early supporter of
the Group of Seven, she also published articles in the *Bookman* by Lawren

Harris and other Group members. She exhibited at the influential Wembley
exhibition in Britain in 1926, and in 1928 was invited to exhibit work in the
Group of Seven exhibition in the Art Gallery of Toronto. In 1930 she
exhibited at the Corcoran Gallery of Art in Washington, DC and at the
Baltimore Museum of Art. In 1934 she married Lawren Harris, and they
lived in Hanover, New Hampshire and Santa Fe, New Mexico, before
moving to Vancouver, BC in 1940.

The Museum London in London, Ontario has requested that this painting
be shown in its upcoming exhibition *Intimate Circle: The F.B. Housser
Memorial Art Collection* on July 26 to September 17, 2005. This loan has not
been promised to this exhibition, and its inclusion is entirely up to the
purchaser.

ESTIMATE: $4,000 ~ 6,000

86

86   LAWREN STEWART HARRIS
BCSFA G7 OSA PRCA 1885 ~ 1970

Toronto Outskirts, Houses Group No. VI

oil on panel, signed and on verso signed three times and titled
variously: *Toronto Outskirts* on the panel / *Houses Group No. VI*
on the artist's label
10 3/4 x 14 in, 27.3 x 35.6 cm

PROVENANCE:
Private Collection, Toronto

LITERATURE:
Jeremy Adamson, *Lawren S. Harris, Urban Scenes and Wilderness
Landscapes, 1906~1930*, Art Gallery of Ontario, 1978, pages 99 and 103

Jeremy Adamson writes: "a breakdown of the entries in the O.S.A., C.N.E.
and Group of Seven exhibitions between March of 1919 and August of
1921 reveals that Harris considered the urban subject his most important
theme…These paintings are among his finest works." Adamson also
points out that the outskirts of Toronto paintings differ from the In the
Ward paintings of the same time period. British working class families
populated the suburban shack towns, while the Ward district was a
European dominated area. The outskirts of Toronto residents had usually
constructed their own homes and as a result had created a strong sense of
self~reliance and community. There is an underlying feeling of optimism
in these series of paintings.

ESTIMATE: $50,000 ~ 60,000

87

88

89

87 WILLIAM GOODRIDGE ROBERTS
OSA RCA 1904 ~ 1974

Looking Out the Window
oil on board, signed and on verso
signed, titled and dated 1959
27 3/4 x 22 in, 70.5 x 55.9 cm

ESTIMATE: $6,000 ~ 8,000

88 J.E.H. (JAMES EDWARD HERVEY) MACDONALD
G7 OSA RCA 1873 ~ 1932

The Barn Door, The Farm, The Township, Ontario (Fred Hardy's Barn)
oil on board, on verso signed, titled and inscribed To Myrtle &
Ralph, June 21, 1921 and This is a companion picture to the one in the
McMichael Collection at Kleinburg Ont., titled "Fred Hardy's Barn"
10 1/4 x 8 in, 26 x 20.3 cm

PROVENANCE:
J.E.H. MacDonald gave this painting as a wedding gift to Myrtle and
Ralph Hardy on June 21, 1921
By descent to the present Private Collection, Vancouver

Sold together with memorabilia ~ cards sent between the MacDonald and
Hardy families; four books with drawings by Thoreau MacDonald: House
and Barn, Farm Drawings, A Year on the Farm and Some Tools of the Pioneers;
the book My High Horse by J.E.H. MacDonald and a 1937 catalogue of a
J.E.H. MacDonald exhibition at Mellors Galleries, Toronto.

ESTIMATE: $6,000 ~ 8,000

89 MAXWELL BENNETT BATES
ARCA ASA CGP CSW 1906 ~ 1980

Farmhouse, Near Calgary
oil on board, signed and on verso
titled and dated 1964
20 x 16 in, 50.8 x 40.6 cm

PROVENANCE:
Canadian Art Galleries, Calgary
Private Collection, Toronto

ESTIMATE: $5,500 ~ 6,500

90 TOM (THOMAS) KEITH ROBERTS
OSA RCA 1909 ~ 1998

Mood of March
oil on board, signed
18 1/2 x 30 in, 47 x 76.2 cm

PROVENANCE:
Private Collection, Toronto

ESTIMATE: $3,500 ~ 4,500

91

93

92

94

95

91 A.Y. (ALEXANDER YOUNG) JACKSON
CGP G7 OSA RCA RSA 1882 ~ 1974

Sugar Shanty; Landscape

double~sided oil on panel, signed and on verso signed,
titled and inscribed *Studio Bldg., Toronto*
10 1/2 x 13 1/2 in, 26.7 x 34.3 cm

EXHIBITED:
YMCA Exhibition

ESTIMATE: $18,000 ~ 22,000

92 AARON ALLAN EDSON
OSA RCA 1846 ~ 1888

Sunlit Forest Path

oil on canvas on board, signed, circa 1880
15 x 10 1/2 in, 38.1 x 26.7 cm

PROVENANCE:
Nora Collyer, Montreal (Beaver Hall artist)
By descent to the present Private Collection, Victoria

ESTIMATE: $3,000 ~ 4,000

93 A.Y. (ALEXANDER YOUNG) JACKSON
CGP G7 OSA RCA RSA 1882 ~ 1974

Lutheran Church, Rosenthal, Ontario

oil on panel, signed and on verso signed and titled
10 1/2 x 13 1/2 in, 26.7 x 34.3 cm

PROVENANCE:
Dominion Gallery, Montreal
By descent to the present Private Collection, Toronto

ESTIMATE: $10,000 ~ 15,000

94 A.Y. (ALEXANDER YOUNG) JACKSON
CGP G7 OSA RCA RSA 1882 ~ 1974

Indian House, Port Simpson, BC

oil on panel, signed and on verso titled and dated 1926
on the McCready Gallery label
10 1/2 x 8 1/2 in, 26.7 x 21.6 cm

PROVENANCE:
Dr. Marius Barbeau
McCready Gallery, Toronto
Kenneth G. Heffel Fine Art Inc., Vancouver
Private Collection, Vancouver

LITERATURE:
Naomi Jackson Groves, *A.Y.'s Canada*, 1968, page 168

This house belonged to Mrs. Musgrave and it was "one of the finest grand
houses in [Port Simpson]...It was built by one of the coastal Tsimsians
with the money from furs and salmon, and from ample returns on
potlatches, some time before 1900."

ESTIMATE: $15,000 ~ 20,000

95 CLAYTON ANDERSON
1964 ~

Last Light on the Gander

acrylic on board, signed and dated 2005 and on verso
signed, titled and dated
24 x 60 in, 61 x 152.4 cm

ESTIMATE: $4,000 ~ 6,000

96

96   A.Y. (ALEXANDER YOUNG) JACKSON
CGP G7 OSA RCA RSA 1882 ~ 1974

Barrenlands Near Lake Atnick
oil on canvas, signed and on verso titled and dated 1961
25 x 32 in, 63.5 x 81.3 cm

PROVENANCE:
Dominion Gallery, Montreal; Private Collection, Vancouver

LITERATURE:
Dennis Reid, *Alberta Rhythm: The Later Work of A.Y. Jackson*, Art Gallery of
Ontario, 1982, pages 32 and 33, the 1959 sketch for this work entitled
Near Atnick Lake, Northwest Territories reproduced page 26

The oil on panel sketch for this colourful large canvas was painted during
a trip Jackson made with Maurice Haycock from August through

September of 1959 that ranged from Lake Athabaska in northern
Saskatchewan to Great Slave Lake and Port Radium on Great Bear Lake.
From there they traveled by helicopter to Hornby Bay and Atnick Lake
and Lake Rouvière in the Barren Lands between the Teshierpi Mountains
and the Dease River. Reid writes, "They camped for a week at Lake
Rouvière and Jackson brought back wonderful pieces from there and
Atnick Lake, rich, vibrant colour studies of the visually remarkable
country." Reid also discusses the qualities of the canvases that resulted
from this trip, with their "free sketch~like handling, the delight in various
textures, from coarse grit to silky smoothness, and the strange, intense
colours. The colours are unforgettable. Strident, but in close harmony,
they call the tune for a dream~like dance, as the twisting forms and
rippling contours celebrate the cycle of survival."

ESTIMATE: $35,000 ~ 45,000

97a

97b

99

97 J.E.H. (JAMES EDWARD HERVEY) MACDONALD

G7 OSA RCA 1873 ~ 1932

Two Works

a) High Park

tempera on artist's board, on verso
signed, titled and inscribed *about 1910*
3 5/8 x 5 in, 9.3 x 12.7 cm

b) Shack in Winter

tempera on artist's board
5 1/2 x 3 1/2 in, 14 x 8.9 cm

PROVENANCE:

Acquired directly from Thoreau MacDonald, Toronto (1969),
by the present Private Collector, Toronto

Please note: both works are unframed.

ESTIMATE: $6,000 ~ 8,000

98 STANLEY MOREL COSGROVE

CGP QMG RCA 1911 ~ 2002

Beach at Latuque

oil on canvas board, signed, circa 1964
13 1/2 x 17 1/2 in, 34.3 x 44.4 cm

PROVENANCE:

Private Collection, Vancouver

The proceeds of this sale will benefit the programs of the
Vancouver Art Gallery.

ESTIMATE: $2,500 ~ 3,500

99 STANLEY MOREL COSGROVE

CGP QMG RCA 1911 ~ 2002

Landscape, Latuque

oil on canvas board, signed and on verso titled, circa 1960
20 x 16 in, 50.8 x 40.6 cm

PROVENANCE:

Dominion Gallery, Montreal
Private Collection, Vancouver

The proceeds of this sale will benefit the programs of the
Vancouver Art Gallery.

ESTIMATE: $3,500 ~ 4,500

98

100

100 A.Y. (ALEXANDER YOUNG) JACKSON
CGP G7 OSA RCA RSA 1882 ~ 1974

Go Home Bay
oil on canvas, signed and on verso signed, titled, dated 1961
and certified by Naomi Jackson Groves Inventory #1867
20 x 26 in, 50.8 x 66 cm

PROVENANCE:
Private Collection, Ontario

LITERATURE:
Naomi Jackson Groves, *A.Y.'s Canada*, 1968, page 108

From 1913 to 1967 Go Home Bay in Georgian Bay was a Jackson
favourite, and he called it his "happy hunting grounds for camping and

fishing at all seasons and in all kinds of weather." The smooth rocks in the
area were ideal for camping, and Jackson brought supplies for cooking,
caught fish and picked berries. Since Dr. MacCallum, the patron of the
Group of Seven, had a house on an island in Go Home Bay, Jackson went
on many canoe and camping trips with him. MacCallum's house was also
the warm centre of much activity, whether it was discussions with other
artists who went there to paint, or community events such as regattas.
When Dr. MacCallum died, his island was purchased by friends of
Jackson's, so Jackson continued to return there. The distinctive small
islands of this area seen in this work, with water softly lapping at their
shores, made wonderful paintings.

ESTIMATE: $25,000 ~ 35,000

101

101   A.Y. (ALEXANDER YOUNG) JACKSON
CGP G7 OSA RCA RSA   1882 ~ 1974

Little Lake, Port Radium
oil on canvas, signed and on verso
signed, titled and dated 1960
16 x 20 in, 40.6 x 50.8 cm

PROVENANCE:
Galerie Walter Klinkhoff Inc., Montreal
Private Collection, Vancouver

LITERATURE:
Dennis Reid, *Alberta Rhythm: The Later Work of A.Y. Jackson*, Art Gallery of
Ontario, 1982, page 17

Jackson traveled to Port Radium on Great Bear Lake in the Northwest

Territories a number of times: 1938, 1949, 1950, 1951 and 1959. In 1938
Gilbert Labine arranged to fly Jackson from Edmonton to his Eldorado
Mine, a uranium mine on Great Bear Lake. Hiking all through the country,
with its "thousands more lakes among thousands more hills", Jackson was
thrilled by its vast scale. Again in 1949, Jackson was flown to the area on the
Eldorado Mine plane, this time joined by the artist Maurice Haycock who
also accompanied Jackson on sketching trips to the area in 1950 and 1959.
Jackson liked the tapestry of rough lichen~covered boulders and the
distinctive patterns of scrub bush in the open land. Jackson lights up this
painting with bright trees that are like candles of colour flickering around
the hills, their dance reflected in the calm lake.

Partial proceeds from the sale of this lot will benefit
BC Children's Hospital.

ESTIMATE: $20,000 ~ 25,000

102

104

102 TONY (ANTONY) SCHERMAN
1950 ~

Still Life

encaustic on canvas, on verso signed and dated 1994
36 x 40 in, 91.4 x 101.6 cm

PROVENANCE:
Gillian Anderson, London, England

ESTIMATE: $15,000 ~ 20,000

103

103 JOSEPH FRANCIS PLASKETT
BCSFA OC RCA   1918 ~

Fruit in Basket

oil on board, signed and dated 1961 and on verso titled
13 x 23 in, 33 x 58.4 cm

PROVENANCE:
Private Collection, Vancouver

The proceeds of this sale will benefit the programs of the
Vancouver Art Gallery.

ESTIMATE: $1,500 ~ 2,000

104 JOHN WENTWORTH RUSSELL
1879 ~ 1959

Mixed Bouquet with Iris

oil on board, signed
24 x 20 1/2 in, 61 x 52.1 cm

PROVENANCE:
Roberts Gallery, Toronto
Private Collection, Toronto

ESTIMATE: $3,000 ~ 4,000

105 FREDERICK SPROSTON CHALLENER
ARCA CSPWC OSA RCA 1869 ~ 1959

Roses
oil on board, signed and dated 1891
10 1/2 x 13 3/4 in, 26.7 x 34.9 cm

ESTIMATE: $3,000 ~ 4,000

105

106

106 RICHARD JACK
RCA 1866 ~ 1952

Still Life
oil on board, signed
20 x 23 3/4 in, 50.8 x 60.3 cm

PROVENANCE:
Continental Galleries of Fine Art, Montreal
Galerie Walter Klinkhoff Inc., Montreal
Kastel Gallery, Montreal
Private Collection, Montreal

ESTIMATE: $6,000 ~ 8,000

107 LUCIUS RICHARD O'BRIEN
OSA PRCA 1832 ~ 1899

Still Life with Roses
watercolour on paper, signed
13 3/4 x 10 3/4 in, 34.9 x 27.3 cm

ESTIMATE: $3,000 ~ 4,000

107

108

108 ARTHUR LISMER
CSPWC G7 OSA RCA   1885 ~ 1969

Still Life with Green Jug
oil on canvas on board, signed
and on verso signed, titled and dated 1952
20 x 16 in, 50.8 x 40.6 cm

PROVENANCE:
By descent to the present Private Collection, Vancouver

LITERATURE:
Lois Darroch, *Bright Land*, 1981, page 141

In 1952, Lismer was an assistant professor in the Department of Fine Art in Montreal's McGill University, and was enjoying a life rich with honours and recognition for both his teaching and his art. His subject matter in

HEFFEL FINE ART AUCTION HOUSE

73

Montreal in the early 1950s took what was, for him, a radical turn to still life. Lois Darroch writes: "Some would say these paintings were after the manner of Cézanne. Certainly they were brilliant in colour, but they were too lively to be imitative." Rich with colour and dense with form, this work is thickly textured and the paint incised with a knife to produce patterns. The view to a landscape through the window and the painting on the wall enlivens this beautiful still life.

ESTIMATE: $20,000 ~ 30,000

109

109 NORA FRANCES ELIZABETH COLLYER
BHHG 1898 ~ 1979

Lilies
oil on board, on verso signed
14 1/4 x 12 in, 35.9 x 30.5 cm

PROVENANCE:
La Galerie Continentale, Montreal
Kastel Gallery, Montreal
Gérard Gorce Beaux~Arts Inc., Montreal

ESTIMATE: $3,000 ~ 4,000

110

110 HENRIETTA MABEL MAY
ARCA BHHG CGP RPS 1884 ~ 1971

Flowers at My Window
oil on canvas board, signed and on verso titled
20 x 16 in, 50.8 x 40.6 cm

PROVENANCE:
Estate of the Artist
Private Collection, Vancouver

Mabel May exhibited extensively throughout her life. As well as showing with the Beaver Hall Group in 1921 and 1922, her work regularly appeared in the National Gallery of Canada's *Annual Exhibition of Canadian Art*, beginning in 1927. Her work also received international exposure in the prestigious Wembley exhibition in England in 1924, as well as the Musée du Jeu de Paume in Paris in 1927, the Corcoran Gallery in Washington, DC in 1930, and the Tate Gallery in London in 1938. In the commercial art gallery world, she exhibited at the Dominion Gallery in Montreal in 1950 and at Roberts Gallery in Toronto in 1951. After she moved to Vancouver in 1950, she had a solo exhibition at the Vancouver Art Gallery in 1952 and showed works at the Art Gallery of Greater Victoria in 1965.

ESTIMATE: $5,000 ~ 7,000

111

111 WILLIAM GOODRIDGE ROBERTS
OSA RCA 1904 ~ 1974

Still Life

oil on board, signed, circa 1950
25 x 32 in, 63.5 x 80.6 cm

PROVENANCE:
Galerie Walter Klinkhoff Inc., Montreal
Private Collection, Montreal

LITERATURE:
Desmond Pacey, "The Goodridge Roberts Exhibition at the Lord
Beaverbrook Art Gallery April 1 ~ 17, 1960", *Canadian Art 17*, July 1960,
page 246

Roberts studied still life painting with Max Weber at New York's Art
Students League in 1926 and 1927, and it remained important subject
matter throughout his life. His still lifes are known for their random yet
graceful placement of everyday objects in quiet, intimate interiors.
Desmond Pacey wrote: "In apparently random collections of objects,
Roberts has managed to find a formality, an elegance, that somehow
transfigures them…In fact one begins to wonder whether Roberts' real
genius, his own particular vision, does not express itself more fully and
naturally in these still lifes than in his more generally valued landscapes."
In this work, expressionistic brush~strokes give energetic movement to
the olive background, in contrast to the stillness of the objects on the
table, and the earthy olive makes the colour of the fruit, flowers and books
even richer.

ESTIMATE: $20,000 ~ 25,000

112

114

112 WILLIAM GOODRIDGE ROBERTS
OSA RCA 1904 ~ 1974

St. Lawrence River at Port~au~Persil

oil on board, signed, 1951
12 x 16 in, 30.5 x 40.6 cm

PROVENANCE:
Roberts Gallery, Toronto
Private Collection, Toronto

LITERATURE:
Goodridge Roberts: A Retrospective Exhibition, The National Gallery of
Canada, 1969, page 48

Roberts painted around Port~au~Persil on the north shore of the St.
Lawrence River east of Quebec City, from June to September 1951. This
view of an abandoned field, encroaching bush and the distant south shore
dates to late in his stay. Jean Paul Lemieux, who was staying at the same
hotel, credited Roberts with restoring his faith in painting that summer.

ESTIMATE: $3,000 ~ 4,000

113 JEAN PAUL LEMIEUX
QMG RCA 1904 ~ 1990

Summer Landscape

oil on panel, signed and dated 1950
8 x 10 in, 20.3 x 25.4 cm

PROVENANCE:
Canadian Fine Arts Gallery, Toronto
Private Collection, Quebec

ESTIMATE: $4,000 ~ 5,000

114 LAWRENCE ARTHUR COLLEY PANTON
OSA RCA 1894 ~ 1954

Sentinels in the Spring in the North Country

oil on canvas, signed and on verso signed and titled
14 x 18 1/2 in, 35.6 x 47 cm

PROVENANCE:
By descent to the present Private Collection, Toronto

ESTIMATE: $1,500 ~ 2,000

113

115

115 FRANK (FRANZ) HANS JOHNSTON
ARCA CSPWC G7 OSA 1888 ~ 1949

Spruce Sentinels, Algoma, Ontario

tempera on paper board, signed *Francis H. Johnston* and dated
1918 and on verso titled and inscribed *This painting was made
on the spot during a trip in the wilds of Algoma, in the autumn of
1918 ~ to be exact Sept. 23rd. The view is taken near the Algoma
Central Railway about 96 miles north of Sault Ste. Marie, Ont.,
and is typical of the country throughout northern Ontario.*
22 x 16 in, 55.9 x 40.6 cm

PROVENANCE:
Private Collection, Alberta

LITERATURE:
Roger Burford Mason, *A Grand Eye for Glory*, 1998, pages 31 and 37

In the fall of 1918 Johnston went on the first of four famous boxcar trips
taken by various members of the Group of Seven, and this rail car journey
up to Sault St. Marie to paint Algoma country was the beginning of an art
history legend. On this trip, Johnston was in the company of Lawren
Harris, J.E.H. MacDonald and their patron Dr. MacCallum. Johnston had
been encouraged to join them by Sir Edmund Walker, a banker and
patron of the arts. It was a time of discovery and companionship, with the
sharing of criticism, encouragement and discussion. Tempera was
Johnston's predominant medium, one in which he "became widely
acknowledged as a master practitioner. He used it for most of his best
paintings." An exhibition of this Algoma work by the three painters was
held in The Grange in May of 1919, and it was a tremendous success.

ESTIMATE: $15,000 ~ 20,000

116 WILLIAM JOHN BERTRAM NEWCOMBE
CSGA CSW 1907 ~ 1969

Mexican Country View

oil on canvas, signed and on verso
signed, titled and dated 1946
20 x 24 in, 50.8 x 61 cm

PROVENANCE:
Private Collection, Vancouver

The proceeds of this sale will benefit the programs of the
Vancouver Art Gallery.

ESTIMATE: $2,500 ~ 3,500

117

117 FREDERICK STANLEY HAINES
OSA PRCA 1879 ~ 1960

Early Autumn

oil on board, signed, circa 1930
10 x 12 in, 25.4 x 30.5 cm

ESTIMATE: $2,500 ~ 3,000

116

118

118   MAURICE GALBRAITH CULLEN
RCA   1866 ~ 1934

Summer on the Cache River

oil on board, signed and on verso titled
and stamped *Cullen Inventory #800*
11 x 13 1/2 in, 27.9 x 34.3 cm

PROVENANCE:
Dominion Gallery, Montreal
The Art Emporium, Vancouver, 1976
Private Collection, Vancouver

ESTIMATE: $10,000 ~ 15,000

120

119

119   FRANK (FRANZ) HANS JOHNSTON
ARCA CSPWC G7 OSA   1888 ~ 1949

Welcome Spring

oil on board, signed and on verso titled on the artist's label
9 1/4 x 12 1/4 in, 23.5 x 31.1 cm

PROVENANCE:
Eaton Galleries, Toronto
Private Collection, Toronto

ESTIMATE: $5,000 ~ 7,000

120   MAURICE GALBRAITH CULLEN
RCA   1866 ~ 1934

A Bend in the River

oil on canvas, signed and dated indistinctly and on verso
certified by Cullen Inventory #918
12 3/4 x 18 in, 32.4 x 45.7 cm

PROVENANCE:
Private Collection, Quebec

Maurice Cullen was a pioneer of Canadian impressionist painting, with a
profound influence on landscape art. He is perhaps best~known for his
summer and winter landscapes along the St. Lawrence River near Quebec
City and Beaupré. He was instrumental in establishing an identifiably
"Canadian" type of landscape and his practice of sketching and painting
outdoors, inspired by the impressionists and their 19th Century European
contemporaries, was followed by that of other great Canadian landscape
painters, among them A.Y. Jackson. Cullen's *A Bend in the River*
exemplifies his use of this technique, and through changing tonalities of
colour in the sky and river, he creates a dramatic visual affect.

ESTIMATE: $10,000 ~ 15,000

121

123

121   W.P. (WILLIAM PERCIVAL) WESTON
ARCA BCSFA CGP 1879 ~ 1967

Fraser Canyon

oil on board, signed and dated 1963 and on verso titled
13 x 15 3/4 in, 33 x 40 cm

PROVENANCE:
Estate of the Artist, Vancouver

ESTIMATE: $3,000 ~ 4,000

122   A.J. (ALFRED JOSEPH) CASSON
CSPWC G7 POSA PRCA 1898 ~ 1992

Lake Baptiste

oil on board, signed and on verso signed and titled, circa 1942
9 1/4 x 11 1/4 in, 23.5 x 28.6 cm

PROVENANCE:
Roberts Gallery, Toronto; Private Collection, Toronto

LITERATURE:
Charles C. Hill, *The Group of Seven: Art for a Nation*, 1995, page 251

A.J. Casson became the seventh member of the Group of Seven in 1926.
Unlike the other members of the group, Casson's favourite subject matter
was consistently the rural scenes of southern Ontario. By painting small
Ontario villages Casson hoped to bring the same kind of recognition to
rural Ontario as Jackson had given Quebec. Charles Hill praises Casson for
his use of "Ontarian imagery" and declares that Casson's "inclusion [in the
Group of Seven] would further the 'academicization' of the Group's
aesthetic." As exemplified in *Lake Baptiste*, Casson's work is characterized
by his refined technique, graceful expression and unique use of colour.

ESTIMATE: $15,000 ~ 18,000

123   FRANK SHIRLEY PANABAKER
ARCA 1904 ~ 1992

Summer, Georgian Bay

oil on board, signed and on verso titled
16 x 20 in, 40.6 x 50.8 cm

PROVENANCE:
The Fine Art Galleries, T. Eaton Co., Toronto
Private Collection, Vancouver

Partial proceeds from the sale of this lot will benefit
BC Children's Hospital.

ESTIMATE: $1,800 ~ 2,200

122

124

124 W.P. (WILLIAM PERCIVAL) WESTON
ARCA BCSFA CGP 1879 ~ 1967

Arbutus
oil on canvas, signed and on verso signed and titled, 1943
30 x 37 in, 76.2 x 94 cm

PROVENANCE:
Estate of the Artist, Vancouver

LITERATURE:
Ian Thom, *W.P. Weston*, The Art Gallery of Greater Victoria, 1980, pages 9 and 13

EXHIBITED:
British Columbia Society of Fine Arts, *33rd Exhibition*, 1943, catalogue #65
Vancouver Art Gallery, *W.P. Weston*, 1946, catalogue #55

Weston often painted trees, admiring their resilience and character. He stated that "all these forms have been affected by and moulded by the elements ~ wind, rain, frost and snow in one way or another, e.g.,…changes in structure in living forms. The study of this is most interesting and has been the main force behind all my drawings and paintings." The arbutus tree, a distinctive West Coast evergreen that often grows on sea bluffs, has the resilience to survive harsh climatic conditions. Clinging to rough terrain and searching for sunlight causes its unique gnarled growth patterns. The tree may even allow part of itself to die during drought. It does, however, store water in burls, which Weston shows at the base of the trees.

This work is typical of Weston's mature style, which, as Ian Thom writes, "owes more to the design motifs of art nouveau/deco, Japanese pattern books and Weston himself than to artists in the east…[and shows] the use of heavy opaque brush~strokes, a 'cool, palpitating and luminous' use of colour, a strong sense of mass and a linear, decorative design." In this strong painting, Weston uses the shadows of the branches on the carpet of moss like reflections in water, delighting in the sculptural shapes. The distinctive orange~red of the smooth trunks stands in dramatic contrast to the green around it. Weston shows this arbutus grove, a beautiful symbol of the West Coast, exuding a powerful life force.

ESTIMATE: $25,000 ~ 30,000

125

125 J.E.H. (JAMES EDWARD HERVEY) MACDONALD
G7 OSA RCA 1873 ~ 1932

Algoma Bush
oil on board, initialed and on verso signed and titled
8 1/2 x 10 1/2 in, 21.6 x 26.7 cm

PROVENANCE:
Galerie Walter Klinkhoff Inc., Montreal
Peter Ohler Fine Art, Vancouver; Private Collection, Toronto

ESTIMATE: $15,000 ~ 20,000

126 HENRIETTA MABEL MAY
ARCA BHHG CGP RPS 1884 ~ 1971

Trees
oil on canvas board, signed
24 x 20 in, 61 x 50.8 cm

PROVENANCE:
Estate of the Artist; Private Collection, Vancouver

ESTIMATE: $6,000 ~ 8,000

127

127 FRANK (FRANZ) HANS JOHNSTON
ARCA CSPWC G7 OSA 1888 ~ 1949

Spruce Island
tempera on paper board, signed *Frank H. Johnston* and on verso titled and inscribed *This picture was painted on the spot, on a bright autumn morning in northern Ontario. It gives an idea of the charming form of the Ontario spruce.*, 1918
7 1/4 x 10 in, 18.4 x 25.4 cm

ESTIMATE: $6,000 ~ 8,000

126

128 EMILY CARR

BCSFA RCA 1871 ~ 1945

Summer, Mount Douglas (No.13)

oil on paper on board, signed and dated 1942 and on verso titled and inscribed *sold, Miss Ann Barry*, also inscribed with the numbers *13* and *17*
36 x 24 in, 91.4 x 61 cm

PROVENANCE:
Acquired from a Vancouver Art Gallery exhibition circa 1940s by Ms. Anne Barry; By descent to Anne Barry's niece, Vancouver

LITERATURE:
Edythe Hembroff~Schleicher, *Emily Carr: The Untold Story*, 1978, page 39
BC Archives, letter to Ira Dilworth, August 2, 1942

EXHIBITED:
The Vancouver Art Gallery, circa 1942, label on verso

The later years of Carr's life were marked by a return to the subject matter that had interested her all of her life, the forests of British Columbia. In August of 1942 Emily Carr took her last sketching trip. During a period of ten days in Mount Douglas Park on the outskirts of Victoria, she "produced fifteen large oil on paper sketches (and a number of smaller ones)". These oil on paper sketches, of which this is one, were some of the most radiant works that she ever painted. She wrote to Ira Dilworth that the rented "cabin is bliss", and the sketches have a freshness and vigour which suggests that she was fully engaged in her work. *Summer, Mount Douglas* is remarkable for the sureness and fluidity of its handling. Carr, who had used the diluted oil medium for almost a decade at this point, treats her subject with an élan and confidence that suggests her delight in the subject. Here we see her pleasure in the life of the forest ~ the brush~strokes of the foliage suggest the shimmer of the trees in a warm summer breeze. The brightness of the light greens gives the feeling of light filtering down into the forest floor, illuminating the wall of foliage in the background. Paper left bare along the edges of the tree trunks and in slivers along branches further acts as a device to bring light into the layers of green forest. The work rejoices in the forest in a way that was important to Carr, reflecting the power, energy and vitality of the natural world.

ESTIMATE: $125,000 ~ 175,000

129 EMILY CARR

BCSFA RCA 1871 ~ 1945

Grey Forest

oil on paper on board, signed with estate stamp and on verso titled, circa 1932
36 x 23 in, 91.4 x 58.4 cm

PROVENANCE:
Dominion Gallery, Montreal; By descent to a Private Collection, Montreal; Private Collection, Toronto

129

LITERATURE:
Emily Carr, *Hundreds and Thousands: The Journals of Emily Carr*, 1966, pages 141 and 142

The medium of oil on paper allowed Emily Carr a greater freedom in her painting of the landscape in that she was able to take her materials out onto the land and capture nature immediately and directly. In this strong work Carr delves into the energy and rhythm of forest and land. Tree forms dance above curving land forms that mount layer upon layer into mountains. Although the work is dense with form, the viewpoint is lofty, giving a sense of space between the viewer and the mountains. Carr's choice of black and white and her use of sweeping brush~strokes in this painting places powerful emphasis on the dancing energy that animates this landscape.

ESTIMATE: $60,000 ~ 80,000

130

132

131

133

130 GEORGE AGNEW REID
OSA PRCA 1860 ~ 1947

The Pond
oil on board, signed and dated indistinctly 1917
and on verso signed and titled
10 x 12 in, 25.4 x 30.5 cm
ESTIMATE: $3,000 ~ 4,000

131 ARTHUR LISMER
CSPWC G7 OSA RCA 1885 ~ 1969

Forest Interior, Vancouver Island
oil on board, signed, 1955
16 x 12 in, 40.6 x 30.5 cm

PROVENANCE:
Galerie Walter Klinkhoff Inc., Montreal
Galerie Martal, Montreal
Private Collection, Toronto

A 1977 photograph certificate of authenticity by
Galerie Walter Klinkhoff accompanies this work.

ESTIMATE: $9,000 ~ 12,000

132 WILLIAM GOODRIDGE ROBERTS
OSA RCA 1904 ~ 1974

Tree Trunks in the Woods
oil on board, signed and on verso titled
and dated 1960 on a gallery label
15 x 18 in, 38.1 x 45.7 cm

PROVENANCE:
Roberts Gallery, Toronto
Private Collection, Toronto

ESTIMATE: $4,000 ~ 5,000

133 JEAN~PHILIPPE DALLAIRE
QMG 1916 ~ 1965

Sousmarine
oil on paper, dated 1957
and on verso titled on a label
17 x 13 1/4 in, 43.2 x 33.7 cm

PROVENANCE:
Galerie Agnès LeFort, Montreal

EXHIBITED:
Galerie Agnès LeFort, Montreal, *Exposition Camp Musical JMC*, 1957

ESTIMATE: $3,000 ~ 4,000

134

134 W.P. (WILLIAM PERCIVAL) WESTON
ARCA BCSFA CGP 1879 ~ 1967

Alouette River
oil on board, signed and on verso signed, titled and dated 1966
13 x 16 in, 33 x 40.6 cm
ESTIMATE: $3,000 ~ 4,000

135

135 W.P. (WILLIAM PERCIVAL) WESTON
ARCA BCSFA CGP 1879 ~ 1967

The Garden Pool
oil on board, signed and on verso signed, titled and dated 1962
16 1/2 x 20 in, 41.9 x 50.8 cm
ESTIMATE: $3,000 ~ 4,000

136 E.J. (EDWARD JOHN) HUGHES
BCSFA RCA 1913 ~

Low Tide, Qualicum

oil on canvas, signed and dated 1950 and on verso signed, titled and dated November 12, 1949 ~ June 26, 1950
20 x 26 in, 50.8 x 66 cm

PROVENANCE:
Dominion Gallery, Montreal
Emme Frankenberg, Montreal
By descent to the present Private Collection, Ontario

LITERATURE:
Doris Shadbolt, *E.J. Hughes*, Vancouver Art Gallery, 1967, reproduced catalogue #15

EXHIBITED:
Vancouver Art Gallery, *E.J. Hughes*, 1967, catalogue #15

When E.J. Hughes returned to British Columbia from his duties as an Official War Artist in 1946, he began a series of paintings of the coast of British Columbia that are among the most singular paintings ever produced in Canada. Other artists soon recognized his work, most notably Lawren Harris, who recommended him to the National Gallery of Canada and to Hart House. By 1950 he had major paintings in public collections in Vancouver, Toronto and Ottawa. Harris also supported his work through the awarding of an Emily Carr Scholarship, which allowed Hughes to sketch around Vancouver Island in 1947 and 1948. Drawings done during this period served as source material for his work for several years. Although other artists recognized him, it was difficult for Hughes to make a go of a career because he was a very deliberate painter. The dates on the back of the canvas covering a period of over seven months suggest the care that Hughes brought to all of his images. *Low Tide, Qualicum* is the result of a careful process of distillation and refinement; there is nothing casual or haphazard about it. His care is equally reflected in the development and organization of the composition ~ the positioning of the figures, the use of light and dark, the patterns of the water surfaces ~ shimmering or waves, even the placement and colour of the buckets that the children use, all are part of a dense and closely~knit fabric. Hughes is sometimes considered a naïve painter but there is nothing naïve about his work ~ if things look the way they do, it is because he wanted them to look that way. It was important for Hughes that the work be read clearly and he was quite willing to distort "reality" to ensure that his point was made. Two examples of this are particularly striking in this painting ~ the depiction of the raft or float which rests on the sand (because the tide is out) and the depiction of the sky in relation to the background mountains. The viewpoint of the raft is strangely distorted. We would not see it this way if our viewpoint were consistent with seeing the silhouettes of the boats. Also, there is the question of the chain. It is an extremely effective colour accent and we read the colour as rust, but it is much more likely that the chain on a raft would be covered with seaweed and barnacles and dull in colour, rather than vivid orange~brown. The silhouette of the mountain range is striking and almost sinister, but Hughes is careful to counter that darkness with patches of light in the clouds and behind the highest point of the mountains. The whole composition is an extraordinary exercise in artifice, each element precisely placed and balanced in colour and form within the whole. It is, however, artifice of the most exceptional sort because it convinces us of a larger truth ~ that the world is a place of exceptional beauty and we have an important place within it.

ESTIMATE: $125,000 ~ 175,000

137

138

139

137 HELEN GALLOWAY MCNICOLL
ARCA RBA 1879 ~ 1915

Fishing Boats at Anchor

oil on canvas, circa 1909
14 x 18 1/2 in, 35.6 x 47 cm

PROVENANCE:
Private Collection, Toronto

LITERATURE:
Natalie Luckyj, *Helen McNicoll*, Art Gallery of Ontario, 1999, page 42

Luckyj writes, "In 1905 McNicoll enrolled in Julius Olsson's School of Landscape and Sea Painting in St. Ives. She took to Algernon Talmage, the modest, reserved… principal of the school. A Cornishman who had trained in London under Sir Hubert Herkomer in Herefordshire, Talmage stressed professionalism and the importance of open~air study." No doubt her time in this picturesque sea village led to her interest in subject matter such as is depicted in this atmospheric painting.

ESTIMATE: $10,000 ~ 15,000

138 JACK LEONARD SHADBOLT
BCSFA CGP RCA 1909 ~ 1998

Fishing Boats, Cornwall, England

watercolour on paper, signed and dated 1945
12 1/2 x 17 1/2 in, 31.7 x 44.4 cm

PROVENANCE:
Betty Shadbolt (the Artist's sister), Vancouver
Gift to the present Private Collector, Vancouver

ESTIMATE: $6,000 ~ 8,000

139 CHRISTOPHER PRATT
RCA 1935 ~

Still Shore

watercolour and graphite on paper, signed, circa 1963
14 x 18 in, 35.6 x 45.7 cm

PROVENANCE:
Private Collection, St. Catherines, Ontario

LITERATURE:
David P. Silcox and Meriké Weiler, *Christopher Pratt*, 1982, pages 17 and 46

Pratt is one of Canada's most important realist painters, and his life in Newfoundland is reflected in his subject matter. Silcox writes, "Pratt has three areas of serious concentration: fishing, sailing and painting." This peaceful scene features a boat, of which Pratt writes, "I have always loved boats. When I was a boy they were far more common, and far more important than cars. They said Newfoundland to me."

ESTIMATE: $4,000 ~ 5,000

140 A.Y. (ALEXANDER YOUNG) JACKSON
CGP G7 OSA RCA RSA 1882 ~ 1974

The Radium Gilbert at Sawmill Bay, Great Bear Lake
oil on panel, signed and on verso
signed, titled twice and dated 1949
10 1/2 x 13 1/2 in, 26.7 x 34.3 cm

PROVENANCE:
Acquired directly from the Artist
By descent to the present Private Collection, Ontario

Jackson had met Hugh Keenleyside, Deputy Minister of the Department of Resources and Development in Ottawa, which led to a 1949 commission to produce paintings of the region around Yellowknife on Great Slave Lake. Flying first to Port Radium on Great Bear Lake, Jackson was glad to re~visit the area which he had last seen in 1938. Fellow artist and mineralogist Maurice Haycock, also with the government department at that time, joined him in his sketching of the area.

ESTIMATE: $12,000 ~ 15,000

140

141 HORACE CHAMPAGNE
1937 ~

The Harbour
pastel on paper, signed and on verso titled
17 1/2 x 23 1/2 in, 44.4 x 59.7 cm

ESTIMATE: $4,000 ~ 6,000

141

142 GERTRUDE SPURR CUTTS
ARCA OSA 1858 ~ 1941

Sorting the Catch
oil on canvas, signed and dated 1900
18 x 24 in, 45.7 x 61 cm

Cutts was born in England and studied in London at the Lambeth School of Art. In 1890, she moved to Toronto to join her family. Already an accomplished artist, having shown with the Royal Society of British Artists and the Society of Women Artists, she opened a studio in Toronto, and became active in the art community. She became a member of the Toronto Art Students' League, and exhibited with the Ontario Society of Artists, the Art Association of Montreal and the Royal Canadian Academy of Arts, as well as in international shows in the United States. In 1909 she married the painter William Cutts, and in 1915 they settled in Port Perry, Ontario.

ESTIMATE: $4,000 ~ 5,000

142

143

143 E.J. (EDWARD JOHN) HUGHES
BCSFA RCA 1913 ~

Departure Bay
oil on canvas, signed and dated 1969
and on verso signed, titled and dated
32 x 40 in, 81.3 x 101.6 cm

PROVENANCE:
Dominion Gallery, Montreal; Private Collection, Montreal

More than any other painter, E.J. Hughes is identified with the coastal landscape of British Columbia. The harbour of Departure Bay, Nanaimo has been a subject of Hughes's work since the 1940s. In this image he has reduced the marine traffic which animates the harbour to small accent points within the larger composition and chosen to concentrate on the foreshore, notably the logs and shingle beach, the expanse of the water and the complex wave patterns upon it and the overarching sky. As in many of his works the close attention that Hughes pays to the foreground elements creates a large~scale still life composition. This still life also serves to bridge the spatial gap between the space of the viewer and the space of the image itself. Interestingly, the "action" of the work ~ the marine traffic ~ is almost all at or near the horizon line. Each of the elements on the horizon ~ ferry, lighthouses, barge or freighter ~ provides a point of visual interest to animate the division between the expanse of the water, which dominates the image, and the sky. One of the most striking aspects of this work is Hughes's decision to allow the central third of the composition to consist of wave pattern. This expanse is broken only on the left by the floating boathouse. The fact that the work is, nevertheless, a fascinating and successful one is a tribute to Hughes's exceptional skills as a painter of water.

ESTIMATE: $100,000 ~ 150,000

144

144 E.J. (EDWARD JOHN) HUGHES
BCSFA RCA 1913 ~

The Imperial Nanaimo
watercolour on paper, signed and dated 1961
12 x 16 in, 30.5 x 40.6 cm

PROVENANCE:
Dominion Gallery, Montreal
The Vincent Price Gallery of Fine Art at Sears
Acquired by the present Private Vancouver Collector in the early 1960s

LITERATURE:
Ian M. Thom, *E.J. Hughes*, 2002, page 143

In 1953, Hughes was approached to do illustrations by *The Lamp*, a
publication of the Standard Oil Company. In the summer of that year,
Hughes journeyed up the British Columbia coast, to Namu, Echo Bay, and
Minstrel and Gilford Islands on the Standard Oil ship *Imperial Nanaimo*.
The thirty~nine drawings that he did on this trip formed the basis for five

paintings that would be reproduced in *The Lamp*. The *Imperial Nanaimo* at
dock was the central image of the fine 1953 canvas *Echo Bay, BC*. This
work, also a dock scene, is full of the colourful details of everyday life in a
small coastal community. The distinctive mast forms of the ship bring
attention to the dramatic sky, whose warm colours reflect back in the
shimmer of the ocean.

In 1961, Hughes decided to use his pencil drawings rather than his
watercolours as the basis for his oils, and to do more watercolours as
complete works in themselves. Thom writes that Hughes "sought to place
himself within the larger traditions of watercolour painting and to assert
watercolour's importance as an art form."

ESTIMATE: $20,000 ~ 25,000

146

145

145 DAVID LLOYD BLACKWOOD
CPE CSPWC OSA RCA 1941 ~

Fire in Indian Bay
etching, signed, titled, editioned 20/50 and dated 1979
20 x 30 1/2 in, 50.8 x 77.5 cm

LITERATURE:
William Gough, *David Blackwood*, 2001, reproduced page 48

This print depicts a forest fire which threatened the fishing and logging community of Indian Bay at the head of Bonavista Bay in 1961.

ESTIMATE: $4,000 ~ 5,000

146 DAVID LLOYD BLACKWOOD
CPE CSPWC OSA RCA 1941 ~

Hauling Job Sturge's House
etching and aquatint, signed, titled,
editioned 9/50 and dated 1979
12 3/4 x 31 1/2 in, 32.4 x 80 cm

PROVENANCE:
Private Collection, Alberta

LITERATURE:
William Gough, *The Art of David Blackwood*, 1988, reproduced plate 20
E. Annie Proulx, *The Shipping News*, 1993, reproduced on the cover
William Gough, *David Blackwood*, 2001, reproduced pages 32 and 33

Chosen as the cover for Annie Proulx's award~winning novel *The Shipping News*, this important print is a record of an event that Blackwood witnessed in the Newfoundland community of Wesleyville in the 1940s. Houses there were built without foundations, and since resources were scarce, the moving of a house was sometimes undertaken rather than re~building. Job Sturge wanted his house in a new location and enlisted the help of the community to move it. The Union Jack is flying because up until 1949, Newfoundland was a colony of Great Britain. The anchor in the foreground is symbolic of the fishing heritage of the area, and the powerful rays of the sun and the hardy Arctic tern flying overhead are signs of hope.

ESTIMATE: $4,000 ~ 5,000

147 FRANK (FRANZ) HANS JOHNSTON
ARCA CSPWC G7 OSA 1888 ~ 1949

The Lone Gull, Georgian Bay
oil on panel, signed and on verso signed and titled
8 1/2 x 12 in, 21.6 x 30.5 cm

PROVENANCE:
Private Collection, Quebec

ESTIMATE: $5,000 ~ 7,000

147

148 ROBERT WAKEHAM PILOT
OSA PRCA 1898 ~ 1967

View Towards Cap~à~l'Aigle
oil on panel, on verso dated 1949
and certified by Galerie Walter Klinkhoff Inc.
12 1/2 x 16 3/4 in, 31.7 x 42.5 cm

PROVENANCE:
Galerie Walter Klinkhoff Inc., Montreal
Private Collection, Quebec

ESTIMATE: $7,000 ~ 9,000

148

149 ARTHUR LISMER
CSPWC G7 OSA RCA 1885 ~ 1969

Figures on a Beach
oil on board, signed
13 1/2 x 15 1/2 in, 34.3 x 39.4 cm

PROVENANCE:
Private Collection, Toronto

LITERATURE:
Lois Darroch, *Bright Land: A Warm Look at Arthur Lismer*, 1981, page 111

More than any other member of the Group of Seven, Arthur Lismer was drawn to the sea. His images of shoreline and the active water itself date from the early part of his career and continue to appear at intervals throughout his mature work. He did many seascapes in the Maritimes, as he had lived in Halifax during the First World War, and continued to return to visit. He also painted seascapes in British Columbia. Lismer's style had a raw vigour, and his fellow artist Harold Beament commented, "There was a controlled rowdiness in Lismer, a roughness. His turbulence showed through his training." Certainly there is a raw vigour in this colourful beach scene with its dramatic sky, which makes the viewer feel the freshness of wind and water.

ESTIMATE: $9,000 ~ 12,000

149

150

150 E.J. (EDWARD JOHN) HUGHES
BCSFA RCA 1913 ~

West of Williams Lake

oil on canvas, signed and dated 1964
and on verso signed, titled and dated
32 x 45 in, 81.3 x 114.3 cm

PROVENANCE:
Dominion Gallery, Montreal

Hughes is strongly associated with his powerful paintings of the West
Coast. However, in 1956, 1958 and 1963 he traveled to the central and
northern interior of BC, producing powerful images of this distinctive
landscape. The 1956 trip was sponsored by the patron Mrs. Doreen
Norton, while the 1958 and 1963 trips were made possible by Canada
Council grants. The work that resulted from his trips to the interior were
almost equal in number to his West Coast paintings at that time. In this
canvas Hughes emphasizes the curvature of the land and the roll of the
hills typical of this area, echoing the downward slope in the angle of the
streaks of cloud and sculpted cloud forms. Hughes creates wonderful
colour contrasts between the ochre burnt grasses on the hills and the blue
sky and the intense iridescent blue of the small lakes. Each detail is
delineated carefully, from each tiny cow by the lake's edge to each small
bush on the hills. Hughes delights in the vista of this open, rolling land.

ESTIMATE: $45,000 ~ 65,000

151

151   E.J. (EDWARD JOHN) HUGHES
BCSFA RCA 1913 ~

Genoa Bay, Vancouver Island

oil on canvas, signed and dated 1981 and on verso signed, titled and inscribed by E.J. Hughes: *On the east coast of Vancouver Island three miles from here (Duncan, BC) are the small settlements of Maple Bay and Bird's Eye Cove, and a shorter distance from the latter by gravel road is the even smaller settlement of Genoa Bay. The view in the above painting is the only one of the bay obtainable from the road, and the thanks for that are due to someone who has been keeping the saplings cleared as can be seen from the fallen tree trunks at lower left in the painting*
32 x 40 in, 81.3 x 101.6 cm

PROVENANCE:
Dominion Gallery, Montreal
By descent to the present Private Collection, Iowa

LITERATURE:
Ian M. Thom, *E.J. Hughes*, Vancouver Art Gallery, 2002, page 187

Ian Thom writes: "By 1980, E.J. Hughes was the most important landscape painter working in British Columbia…Hughes continued on the course that he had followed in the previous decade, but his importance as a painter was finally becoming more widely accepted." This outstanding painting is very typical of his small coastal harbour scenes with the great attention to detail and love of colour in the brightly painted boats, boathouses, house boats and the jaunty yellow striped sail. The slow ripple of light reflections has the languorous feel of a peaceful day, and the even, somewhat greenish hue of the atmosphere is a light unique to the West Coast. Though there is evidence of movement in the rippling water and sailboat, the scene feels like a moment frozen in time. Hughes shows us a world in which the graceful beauty of nature and the small harbour at Genoa Bay rest in contrast, yet in harmony with each other.

ESTIMATE: $45,000 ~ 55,000

152

155

153

156

154

157

152 SYBIL ANDREWS
CPE 1898 ~ 1992

Boat Building

oil on canvas, signed, circa 1942
22 x 27 in, 55.9 x 68.6 cm

LITERATURE:
Peter White, *Sybil Andrews: Colour Linocuts*, Glenbow Museum, Calgary, 1982, similar work reproduced page 18

In 1942 Sybil Andrews began war work in the yards of the British Power Boat Company at Hythe near Southampton, England. Peter White states, "Although she stopped making linocuts during the war years, this period was not totally unproductive. In her off hours she was able to work on a series of sketches of the shipyards that were later executed as oil paintings."

ESTIMATE: $4,500 ~ 6,500

153 PHILLIP HENRY HOWARD SURREY
RCA 1910 ~ 1990

Bus Ride

oil on canvas, signed and on verso
stamped *Estate of Phillip Surrey*
16 1/4 x 24 in, 40.6 x 61 cm

ESTIMATE: $3,500 ~ 4,500

154 JACK LEONARD SHADBOLT
BCSFA CGP RCA 1909 ~ 1998

Buccaneer Bay

oil on board, on verso signed and titled, 1947
19 x 24 in, 48.3 x 61 cm

PROVENANCE:
Acquired by a friend of the Artist, Vancouver, circa 1950
By descent to the present Private Collection, Vancouver

Shadbolt produced a number of important paintings on a 1947 visit to Buccaneer Bay, which is on the southern tip of Thormanby Island, off the Sunshine Coast of BC.

ESTIMATE: $6,500 ~ 8,500

155 TIKO KERR
1953 ~

North Shore Over Locarno Beach

acrylic on canvas, on verso signed, titled and dated 2005
30 x 40 in, 76.2 x 101.6 cm

ESTIMATE: $3,000 ~ 4,000

156 ADAM SHERRIFF SCOTT
RCA 1887 ~ 1980

Rocky Shoreline

oil on canvas, signed
18 1/8 x 24 in, 46 x 61 cm

ESTIMATE: $1,200 ~ 1,600

157 LAWRENCE ARTHUR COLLEY PANTON
OSA RCA 1894 ~ 1954

Afternoon, St. Margaret's Bay

oil on board, signed and
dated 1949 and on verso titled
13 x 16 in, 33 x 40.6 cm

PROVENANCE:
By descent to the present Private Collection, Toronto

ESTIMATE: $1,000 ~ 1,500

158

158 ILLINGWORTH HOLEY KERR
ASA BCSFA RCA 1905 ~ 1989

Wind Across the Lake

oil on canvas, initialed and on verso signed, circa 1940
30 x 36 in, 76.2 x 91.4 cm

PROVENANCE:
Acquired circa 1940 ~ 1950 by the present Private Collector, Vancouver

ESTIMATE: $4,500 ~ 6,500

159

159 ALEXANDER COLVILLE

OC RCA 1920 ~

Woman with Skiff

acrylic polymer emulsion on board
on verso signed, titled and dated 21 Sept. 1999
17 x 38 in, 43.2 x 96.5 cm

PROVENANCE:
Mira Godard Gallery, Toronto
Heffel Gallery, Vancouver
Private Collection, California

LITERATURE:
Tom Smart, *Alex Colville: Return*, 2003, Art Gallery of Nova Scotia, page 100, reproduced page 101

Graham Metson, "Alex Colville on Alex Colville: Transcription of an interview with Graham Metson, November 1980", *Diary of a War Artist*, 1981

EXHIBITED:
Art Gallery of Nova Scotia, *Alex Colville: Return*, 27 September ~ 30 November, 2003; in 2004 and 2005 traveling to: Beaverbrook Art Gallery, Fredericton, Museum London, University of Toronto Art Centre, the Edmonton Art Gallery and the Mendel Art Gallery, Saskatoon, catalogue #TL2003.47

Smart writes that "Colville's close association of women and boats also figures prominently in his 1999 painting *Woman with Skiff*, an image of a female figure pulling a boat up on to the bank of the tidal plain. The artist came upon this scene one day when he was sailing along the Gaspereau River near Wolfville. *Woman with Skiff* is a very beautiful, balanced image that is intended to convey peacefulness. Colville wanted to capture the idea of people walking on a dyke and the idea that women can, and do, go out to be at peace with nature, to commune with it. 'Women who go alone to a lone place' expresses the feeling of this painting; it is a picture of an adventurous and active person not afraid of being by herself. This, Colville says, represents women in general, and in particular his daughter, Ann, as a kind of heroine figure. In essence, *Woman with Skiff* conveys the longing to be alone."

Colville's landforms are like carved sculptural forms and the water itself seems solid. The boat seems suspended over the water, rather than floating in it. The woman's figure does not cast shadows, and when you look at her feet, she also seems to hover on the shore. Although it is a realist painting, Colville's eye is not strictly photographic. Instead he strips away extraneous detail, and by his use of spatial disassociation, gives a subtle air of surrealism to the work, a place of different perceptual awareness.

ESTIMATE: $125,000 ~ 175,000

160 PAUL~ÉMILE BORDUAS

QMG RCA 1905 ~ 1960

Jardin d'Hiver

oil on canvas, signed, circa 1955
13 x 16 in, 33 x 40.6 cm

PROVENANCE:
Acquired by the present Private Collector from Laing Galleries, Toronto, 1957

LITERATURE:
François~Marc Gagnon, *Paul~Émile Borduas*, 1978, painting listed, pages 439 and 532

Ray Ellenwood, *Egregore: The Montreal Automatist Movement*, 1992, pages 173 and 262

160

Laing Galleries, Toronto, 1957

Jardin d'Hiver is a stunning painting that typifies Borduas's work from his New York Period (1953~1955) and echoes the burst of freedom he experienced following his departure from what he regarded as the stifling environment of Quebec. The early years of the post~war New York cultural scene exposed Borduas to the works of the abstract expressionists and could only have encouraged him to cultivate the aesthetic ideas he espoused in his revolutionary manifesto, the *Refus Global*. Ray Ellenwood asserts that the type of aesthetic identified in the *Refus Global* was "concerned in its painterly expression, particularly the way it expressed itself non~figuratively." Borduas's canvases from his New York period maintain the qualities which were called for in the *Refus Global*, but also begin to show what Ellenwood describes as "an all~over quality they did not have before, developed not through dripping (although he did try that, occasionally) but with small strokes of the palette knife in heavy impasto."

Jardin d'Hiver was one of ten paintings which were purchased from the artist in his studio by the Laing Gallery for exhibition in 1957.

This work will be included in the forthcoming artist's catalogue raisonné compiled by Dr. François~Marc Gagnon.

ESTIMATE: $55,000 ~ 75,000

161

161 JACK LEONARD SHADBOLT
BCSFA CGP RCA 1909 ~ 1998

City Lights
oil on canvas, signed, circa 1957
35 1/2 x 43 in, 90.2 x 109.2 cm

PROVENANCE:
Acquired by the present Private Toronto Collector, 1959

LITERATURE:
Jack Shadbolt to Vancouver School of Art students and colleagues, open
letter from Menton, 6 Nov. 1956
Colin Graham, "A Year in the Sun", *Canadian Art*, Spring 1958

At the end of 1956 and into 1957, Shadbolt was spending a year abroad in
Europe, and was centered in Menton, France, near the Italian border. The
Mediterranean affected him deeply, and he exploded with colour
awareness, writing, "I nearly went mad just out of Toulon…My first
Mediterranean colour ~ cool melon, heliotrope, clear pale mineral
blue…Blacks as rich as loam." Characteristic of the work of this time was
the way he applied paint with a palette knife or sometimes a cardboard strip
to give a built~up sculptural look. Also typical of the painting he did in this
period was the use of a townscape as a starting point for his abstraction.
Colin Graham wrote of these works: "Space is created mainly through the
advancing and receding properties of colour, and it is colour which plays
the major role in the paintings. Chromatically intense, affirmative and
joyous, it now creates not only the space but the light." The revelation of

light and colour that Shadbolt had during his Mediterranean stay had a great impact on his work when he returned to Vancouver.

This painting is one of the finest Shadbolts from this period that we have had the pleasure to offer for sale.

ESTIMATE: $10,000 ~ 15,000

162

162   LEON BELLEFLEUR
QMG   1910 ~

Tour d'Ivoire

oil on canvas, signed and dated 1977
and on verso signed, titled and dated
18 x 15 in, 45.7 x 38.1 cm

PROVENANCE:
Galerie Walter Klinkhoff Inc., Montreal; Private Collection, Toronto

Leon Bellefleur is considered to be one of the forerunners of modern painting in Quebec. In 1942 he signed the *Prisme d'Yeux* art manifesto joining Quebec~based artist contemporaries Pellan, Archambault, De Tonnancour and several others. He subscribed to the surrealist theory of objective accidents, evident in the juxtaposition of forms on his canvases. Bellefleur's *Tour d'Ivoire* evokes an image of interplaying spontaneity, movement, colour and form ~ qualities that were inspired by the drawings of his children.

ESTIMATE: $2,500 ~ 3,500

163

163   JEAN~PAUL RIOPELLE
QMG RCA SCA 1923 ~ 2002

Untitled

gouache on paper, 1956
30 1/4 x 22 1/4 in, 76.8 x 56.5 cm

PROVENANCE:
Private Collection, Vancouver

LITERATURE:
Yseult Riopelle, *Jean~Paul Riopelle: Catalogue Raisonné, Tome 2*, 2004, catalogue #1956.022P.1956, reproduced page 382

Living in Paris in 1956, Riopelle had already become an internationally recognized Canadian abstract painter. Riopelle had two solo exhibitions of his gouaches and watercolours that year, at Gimpel Fils Gallery, London and at the Pierre Matisse Gallery, New York. Riopelle's gouaches from 1956 mark a shift in his approach to works on paper. His earlier watercolours made maximum use of the transparency of the medium. The opaque gouache medium allowed him to more closely replicate the texture of his paintings on canvas and to make reference to the drips that were prominent in his earlier paintings.

ESTIMATE: $15,000 ~ 18,000

164

164   RENÉ MARCIL
1917 ~ 1993

Untitled Abstract

oil on canvas, signed and dated 1966
and on verso signed and dated
50 x 68 in, 127 x 172.7 cm

PROVENANCE:
Collection of Robert and Maud Langevin, Toronto

EXHIBITED:
Kar Gallery of Fine Art, Toronto, 1977

ESTIMATE: $6,000 ~ 8,000

165

165   JACK LEONARD SHADBOLT
BCSFA CGP RCA   1909 ~ 1998

Morning Tide

acrylic on canvas, signed
53 1/2 x 45 in, 135.9 x 114.3 cm

PROVENANCE:
Private Collection, BC

ESTIMATE: $8,000 ~ 10,000

166   JACK LEONARD SHADBOLT
BCSFA CGP RCA   1909 ~ 1998

Full Fathom

acrylic on canvas, signed and dated 1991
49 x 54 in, 124.4 x 137.1 cm

PROVENANCE:
Bau~Xi Gallery, Toronto
Estate of Isabel McLaughlin, Toronto

ESTIMATE: $8,000 ~ 10,000

166

167 WILLIAM PATERSON EWEN
1925 ~ 2002

Full Moon

watercolour on handmade paper
on verso titled and dated 1990
19 x 19 1/2 in, 48.3 x 49.5 cm

PROVENANCE:
Equinox Gallery, Vancouver
Private Collection, Vancouver

LITERATURE:
Matthew Teitelbaum, *Paterson Ewen*, Art Gallery of Ontario, 1996, page 79

Teitelbaum writes: "Since 1971, the moon has been Ewen's most favoured subject, a virtual field in which great and varied states are recorded: a day moon, a night moon, a gibbous moon, a half moon."

ESTIMATE: $6,000 ~ 8,000

167

168 GREGORY RICHARD CURNOE
1936 ~ 1992

*Rocket Ship, Painting
and Linoleum Sample Book*

watercolour & pencil on photograph on paper, signed,
dated April 10 ~ 20, 1981 and inscribed *Montreal*
8 1/4 x 12 3/8 in, 21 x 31.4 cm

PROVENANCE:
Private Collection, Ontario

EXHIBITED:
Art Gallery of Windsor, *Windsor Collects: 150 Years of Canadian Art*,
July ~ September 1997, catalogue #24

ESTIMATE: $2,000 ~ 3,000

168

169 TONY (ANTONY) SCHERMAN
1950 ~

Flying Down to Rio

encaustic on canvas, on verso signed, titled and dated 1981
36 1/4 x 60 in, 91.4 x 152.4 cm

PROVENANCE:
The Mayor Gallery, London, England
Private Collection, Los Angeles
Heffel Fine Art Auction House, November 8, 2001, lot 94
Private Collection, Montreal

ESTIMATE: $14,000 ~ 16,000

169

170

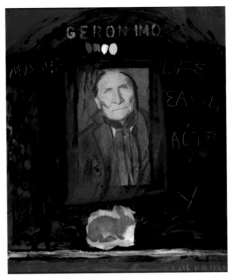

171

170   MAUD LEWIS
1903 ~ 1970

Hauling Logs

oil on board, signed
12 1/4 x 14 1/4 in, 31.1 x 36.2 cm

PROVENANCE:
Acquired directly from the Artist circa 1965 by the present Private
Collector, Vancouver

ESTIMATE: $3,000 ~ 4,000

171   JANE ASH POITRAS
RCA   1951 ~

Manifest Life Eagle Alter ~ Geronimo

mixed media on board, signed
20 x 17 in, 50.8 x 43.2 cm

Jane Ash Poitras's collages bring mass media images of First Nations
people together with abstract backgrounds and text to achieve a
powerfully spiritual effect. Poitras seeks to re~establish an identity for
native peoples, reaching to understand the past through the language of
contemporary art. This work depicts Apache Chief Geronimo.

ESTIMATE: $1,000 ~ 1,500

172   MAUD LEWIS
1903 ~ 1970

Deer in the Snow

oil on board, signed
11 3/4 x 14 in, 29.8 x 35.6 cm

PROVENANCE:
Private Collection, Toronto

ESTIMATE: $4,000 ~ 6,000

172

173

175

173   JANE ASH POITRAS
RCA   1951 ~

Shaman

mixed media on board, signed
36 x 24 in, 91.4 x 61 cm

Jane Ash Poitras was born in Fort Chipewyan, Alberta and is of Cree descent. Adopted at the age of five by a German~Canadian family, it was only as a young woman that she reconnected with her heritage. She has a Masters in Fine Arts from Columbia University in New York, and has been influenced by the collages of Robert Rauschenberg and Kurt Schwitters. Her work explores such political issues as the impact of colonialism on native culture, as well as the spiritual strength of native peoples.

ESTIMATE: $2,000 ~ 3,000

174   MAUD LEWIS
1903 ~ 1970

Covered Bridge with Skaters

oil on board, signed and on verso
inscribed *Kinnear*, circa 1966
12 x 14 1/4 in, 30.5 x 36.2 cm

PROVENANCE:
Private Collection, Ontario

The inscription refers to John Kinnear, who was an artist and friend of Maud Lewis's.

ESTIMATE: $6,000 ~ 8,000

175   MAUD LEWIS
1903 ~ 1970

Hauling Logs, Sandy Cove, Digby Neck, Nova Scotia

oil on board, signed
12 1/4 x 14 1/4 in, 31.1 x 36.2 cm

PROVENANCE:
Acquired directly from the Artist circa 1965 by the present Private Collector, Vancouver

ESTIMATE: $3,000 ~ 4,000

174

177

177   EARLY HAIDA ARTIST
19TH CENTURY

Haida~Form Pipe
argillite relief carving, circa 1830 ~ 1860
1 3/4 x 10 3/4 x 1 in, 4.4 x 27.3 x 2.5 cm

PROVENANCE:
Isaacs Gallery, Toronto
Nancy Poole, Toronto
Private Collection, Toronto

LITERATURE:
Marius Barbeau, *Haida Myths*, National Museum of Canada, 1953, the
Peabody argillite panel reproduced page 94
Peter L. Macnair and Alan L. Hoover, *The Magic Leaves: A History of Haida
Argillite Carving*, Royal British Columbia Museum, 2002 [second
edition], chapter 7

The Haida are renowned for their use of argillite, which is a relatively soft
carbonaceous shale found only on the Queen Charlotte Islands,
principally at Slatechuck Creek. The Haida appear to have started carving
argillite after contact with American and European sailors. Many of the
sailors made informal scrimshaw carvings on their long ocean voyages.
Most of the earliest Haida carvings are of pipes, made for sale and trade.
This one is of an unusually geometric and densely packed design,
stylistically related to an intricately carved argillite panel in the Peabody
Museum in Salem, Massachusetts. The vast majority of surviving argillite
pipes are now in museum collections.

ESTIMATE: $8,000 ~ 10,000

176

176   NUNA PARR
1949 ~

Dancing Bear
dark green serpentine stone sculpture, signed
16 x 12 x 4 in, 40.6 x 30.5 x 10.2 cm

Born in Cape Dorset in 1949 to Kingnimuit parents who were
well~known graphic artists, Parr became a hunter, and his observations
of wildlife naturally led to his interest in carving images of them. Bears are
his most sought~after subject matter, and he often depicts them showing
their playful nature.

ESTIMATE: $3,000 ~ 4,000

178

178 NUNA PARR

1949 ~

Dancing Bear

green serpentine stone sculpture, signed
20 x 18 x 6 in, 50.8 x 45.7 x 15.2 cm

Nuna Parr is particularly known for his beautifully sculpted bears carved
from classic Dorset stone. Although it is more challenging to carve than
soapstone, Parr manages to find balance, proportion, and delicacy in the
unforgiving medium of serpentine stone. The grain and striation of
colours displayed in *Dancing Bear* highlights the natural qualities of the
stone and shows the craftsmanship for which Parr is best known in his
elegantly curved and fluid renditions of wildlife of the far northern
regions of Canada.

ESTIMATE: $6,500 ~ 8,500

179

179 JOHNNY INUKPUK

1911 ~

Woman Working Leather

soapstone sculpture, signed in syllabics, circa 1970
13 3/4 x 8 1/2 x 4 in, 34.9 x 21.6 x 10.2 cm

PROVENANCE:

Canadian Guild of Crafts, Toronto; Private Collection, Toronto

LITERATURE:

Craft Dimensions (the bimonthly magazine published by the Canadian Guild
of Crafts for its members), December 1970, reproduced pages 16 ~ 17
George Swinton, *Eskimo Sculpture: Esquimaude*, 1965, page 130

Johnny Inukpuk, an Inuit sculptor who resides in Inukjuak, has attained
considerable recognition for his work. He is represented in the
collections of prestigious museums such as the National Gallery of
Canada, the Art Gallery of Ontario in Toronto, the Canadian Museum of
Civilization in Hull, Quebec and the Metropolitan Museum of Art in New
York City. George Swinton asserts that Inukpuk's sculptures are "strong
and decisive, with great emphasis on physical and emotional force,
stressing meaning and feeling".

ESTIMATE: $10,000 ~ 12,000

180

181

182

180 NICHOLAS DE GRANDMAISON
ARCA 1892 ~ 1978

Indian Portrait
pastel on paper, signed, circa 1930
14 x 11 1/2 in, 35.6 x 29.2 cm

PROVENANCE:
Private Collection, Washington

Grandmaison is best known as a visual historian of Canada's vanishing indigenous cultures, particularly the Blood, Peigan, Stoney and Blackfoot nations of southern Alberta. He was primarily based in Banff, Alberta, but was also known to have traveled into the United States as far south as Arizona visiting native peoples, seeing them as extended family. He traveled onto the reservations hearing their stories and recording all their nuances of character in his pastels. His own story of displacement instilled in him a great sympathy for their plight as a people, and he saw written in their faces all their history ~ with struggle, dignity and pride intermingled.

ESTIMATE: $6,000 ~ 8,000

181 NICHOLAS DE GRANDMAISON
ARCA 1892 ~ 1978

Blood Indian Iron from Cardston
pastel on paper, signed and on verso titled and inscribed *given to Sonia Clair Grandmaison, 1948, NG*, circa 1940
26 x 20 in, 66 x 50.8 cm

PROVENANCE:
Private Collection, Vancouver

ESTIMATE: $10,000 ~ 15,000

182 NICHOLAS DE GRANDMAISON
ARCA 1892 ~ 1978

Johny Yokom
pastel on paper, signed and titled, circa 1930
14 x 11 1/2 in, 35.6 x 29.2 cm

PROVENANCE:
Private Collection, Washington

Grandmaison was originally of the Russian aristocracy, and was an officer in the Russian Army in WWI. After his release from a prisoner~of~war camp, he found that the Revolution had irrevocably changed Russia, and so he fled to England where he registered under the British Aliens Act and attended art school. In 1923 he immigrated to Canada. On November 27, 1933 he legally changed his name to De Grandmaison and began signing his works that way. As lots 180 and 182 are signed N. Grandmaison, it indicates that they were painted prior to 1933.

ESTIMATE: $6,000 ~ 8,000

183

183   ARTHUR SHILLING
1941 ~ 1986

Dan George

oil on canvas, signed and on verso
dated 1973 and inscribed *Rama*
23 x 21 3/4 in, 58.4 x 55.2 cm

PROVENANCE:
Campbell Framers and Gallery, Toronto
Private Collection, Toronto

Dan George (1899 ~ 1981) was born into the Tsleil~Waututh (Salish)
band on Burrard Reserve in North Vancouver. Until the age of 60 he
worked as a longshoreman and in construction, and was Chief of the
Tsleil~Waututh from 1951 to 1963. Chief Dan George was over 60 when
he became a movie actor. His career began with an acclaimed role in
George Ryga's play *The Ecstasy of Rita Joe*. At 71 he won the prestigious
New York Film Critics award for his role in the film *Little Big Man*, and an
Academy Award nomination for best supporting actor. His success as an
actor and writer catapulted him into the position of spokesman for the
people of Canada's First Nations, and he spoke with dignity of their
plight.

ESTIMATE: $4,000 ~ 5,000

184

184   MARY RITER HAMILTON
1873 ~ 1954

Reflections

oil on canvas, signed and inscribed *Paris*
and on verso inscribed *30*, circa 1905
24 x 19 3/4 in, 61 x 50.2 cm

PROVENANCE:
Private Collection, Vancouver

Hamilton studied portrait painting in Paris under J. Blanche at the Vittie
Academy. In 1905 two of Hamilton's works were accepted at the Paris
Salon, and she continued to show at this annual exhibition.

ESTIMATE: $3,000 ~ 4,000

185a

185b

186

185 HENRIETTA MABEL MAY
ARCA BHHG CGP RPS 1884 ~ 1971

Two Works

a) Two of my Friends
oil on canvas laid down on paper board
signed and on verso signed, titled and dated 1956
9 1/4 x 12 1/2 in, 23.5 x 31.8 cm

b) Study of Two of my Friends
oil on canvas board
12 x 16 in, 30.5 x 40.7 cm

PROVENANCE:
Estate of the Artist
Private Collection, Vancouver

ESTIMATE: $4,000 ~ 6,000

186 BILL (WILLIAM) HADD MCELCHERAN
RCA 1927 ~ 1999

Satisfied
bronze sculpture, signed, editioned 4/9 and dated 1996
30 1/2 x 11 1/4 x 10 7/8 in, 77.5 x 28.6 x 27.6 cm

PROVENANCE:
Private Collection, Toronto

McElcheran is known for his satirical and humorous bronze sculptures of the businessman, dressed in his generic suit and accessories, bustling through his day. Evident in his sculptures is that McElcheran found the comedy in the day~to~day grind of the business world, but viewed his subjects and their struggle for success with compassion and hope. McElcheran's bronze sculptures have been installed in public places in Toronto, Calgary, Italy and Germany.

ESTIMATE: $12,000 ~ 16,000

187

187 HENRI HÉBERT

RCA   1884 ~ 1950

Danseuse au Repos

bronze sculpture, signed and inscribed
Roman Bronze Works, N.Y., 1926
17 3/4 x 5 1/2 x 4 in, 45.1 x 14 x 10.2 cm

PROVENANCE:
Private Collection, Victoria

LITERATURE:
Janet M. Brooke, *Henri Hébert, 1884~1950: Un Sculpteur Moderne*, Musée
du Québec, 2000, reproduced catalogue #51, page 154

ESTIMATE: $6,000 ~ 8,000

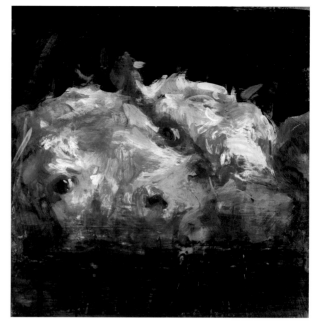

188

188 TONY (ANTONY) SCHERMAN

1950 ~

Io and Friend

encaustic on canvas, on verso signed, titled and dated 1994
24 x 24 in, 61 x 61 cm

PROVENANCE:
Heffel Gallery, Vancouver
Gillian Anderson, London, England

While there has been a long tradition of painting cattle, mostly idealized,
in pastoral landscapes, Scherman takes the unusual step of placing them
in the tradition of portraiture. They are now not part of the landscape, but
"sitters" who are confined by a paddock, gazing out at the viewer, who
must look into the souls of these animals. We become aware of their
situation, their fate, and are confronted with that from which we would
normally remain distant. Scherman has named one of the cattle Io, after
the mortal lover of the Roman God Jupiter, a further reminder of the
worldly fate of these cattle.

ESTIMATE: $8,000 ~ 10,000

189

191

189 HENRI LEOPOLD MASSON
CGP CSPWC OSA QMG RCA 1907 ~ 1996

Ottawa River, Eardley, Quebec

oil on canvas, signed and on verso
signed, titled and dated 1977
18 x 24 in, 45.7 x 61 cm

ESTIMATE: $4,500 ~ 5,500

191 ALBERT JACQUES FRANCK
ARCA CSPWC OSA 1899 ~ 1973

Back of Grenville Street

watercolour on paper, signed and dated 1963
and on verso titled on the artist's label
19 x 24 in, 48.3 x 61 cm

ESTIMATE: $7,000 ~ 8,000

192

190

190 SERGE BRUNONI
1938 ~

Montreal, Devant le Ritz, Sherbrooke Street

acrylic on canvas, signed and on verso titled
30 x 40 in, 76.2 x 101.6 cm

ESTIMATE: $2,500 ~ 3,500

192 HENRI LEOPOLD MASSON
CGP CSPWC OSA QMG RCA 1907 ~ 1996

Near Angers

oil on canvas, signed and on verso
signed, titled and dated 1973
20 x 30 in, 50.8 x 76.2 cm

ESTIMATE: $4,000 ~ 5,000

193

195

193 TERRY TOMALTY

1935 ~

Arcade Street Rink

oil on canvas, signed and on verso
signed, titled and dated 2003
12 x 16 in, 30.5 x 40.6 cm

ESTIMATE: $1,500 ~ 1,800

195 ARMAND TATOSSIAN

RCA 1948 ~

Joueurs de Hockey

oil on canvas, signed and inscribed *R.C.A.*
30 x 40 in, 76.2 x 101.6 cm

ESTIMATE: $4,000 ~ 6,000

194

196

194 RANDOLPH STANLEY HEWTON

BHHG RCA 1888 ~ 1960

Winter Landscape

oil on canvas
20 1/4 x 24 in, 51.4 x 61 cm

ESTIMATE: $10,000 ~ 15,000

196 HENRI LEOPOLD MASSON

CGP CSPWC OSA QMG RCA 1907 ~ 1996

Winter Mood

oil on board, signed and dated 1964 and on verso signed and titled
10 x 12 in, 25.4 x 30.5 cm

ESTIMATE: $1,500 ~ 2,000

197

198

197   GEORGE FRANKLIN ARBUCKLE
OSA PRCA   1909 ~ 2001

The Road into the Village

oil on canvas, signed
20 x 26 in, 50.8 x 66 cm

PROVENANCE:
Private Collection, Quebec

ESTIMATE: $3,500 ~ 4,500

198   A.J. (ALFRED JOSEPH) CASSON
CSPWC G7 POSA PRCA   1898 ~ 1992

On Sheppard Avenue

oil on panel, signed and on verso
signed, titled and dated 1947
9 1/2 x 11 1/4 in, 24.1 x 28.6 cm

PROVENANCE:
Roberts Gallery, Toronto
Kenneth G. Heffel Fine Art Inc., Vancouver
Private Collection, Vancouver

ESTIMATE: $12,000 ~ 16,000

199   RENÉ JEAN RICHARD
1895 ~ 1982

Trapper on the River George, Ungava

oil on board, signed and on verso signed and titled
28 x 31 1/2 in, 71.1 x 80 cm

PROVENANCE:
Galerie Walter Klinkhoff Inc., Montreal; Private Collection, Vancouver

Born in Switzerland, Richard moved to Alberta with his family in 1910 and eventually left home to become a trapper in that province's north. During this time he became acquainted with the people and customs of the north while developing his skills as a painter. The depiction of trappers in the landscape is a common subject for him at this time. This work, with its vibrant colours and energetic brush~strokes, shows the unrelenting nature of Canada's northern wilderness. Richard's work can be found in the collection of the National Gallery of Canada.

Partial proceeds from the sale of this lot will benefit BC Children's Hospital.

ESTIMATE: $4,500 ~ 6,500

199

200

200 HENRI LEOPOLD MASSON
CGP CSPWC OSA QMG RCA 1907 ~ 1996

Parliament Hill from Hull
oil on canvas laid down on board, signed
15 x 18 in, 38.1 x 45.7 cm

PROVENANCE:
Private Collection, Toronto

ESTIMATE: $4,000 ~ 5,000

201 A.Y. (ALEXANDER YOUNG) JACKSON
CGP G7 OSA RCA RSA 1882 ~ 1974

Notre Dame de la Salette, P. Que.
oil on panel, signed and on verso inscribed *Painted in oil at the summer home of Dr. R.A. Starrs Lake Clear, Ontario, from a pencil drawing done at Notre Dame de la Salette, P.Q., Sept. 1965*
10 1/2 x 13 1/2 in, 26.7 x 34.3 cm

PROVENANCE:
Private Collection, Quebec

LITERATURE:
Naomi Jackson Groves, *A.Y.'s Canada*, 1968, page 42

Although Jackson wandered over much of Canada, Quebec villages were his most loved subject matter. As Naomi Jackson Groves writes, "A.Y.'s Quebec works have become so familiar to us Canadians in the course of this century that we usually simply take for granted that 'Quebec looked that way in the olden days,' forgetting that a thing only 'looks like' something after someone has created an image of it and made us familiar with that image. More than any other single Canadian artist during the quarter~century from 1920 on, it has been A.Y. Jackson who has created the image of rural…Quebec."

ESTIMATE: $10,000 ~ 15,000

202

202 HENRI LEOPOLD MASSON
CGP CSPWC OSA QMG RCA 1907 ~ 1996

Freshwater, Newfoundland
oil on board, signed and on verso
signed, titled and dated 1968
12 x 16 in, 30.5 x 40.6 cm

PROVENANCE:
Alexander Fraser Galleries, Vancouver
Private Collection, Vancouver

The proceeds of this sale will benefit the programs of the Vancouver Art Gallery.

ESTIMATE: $3,000 ~ 4,000

201

203

206

204

207

205

208

203 HENRI LEOPOLD MASSON
CGP CSPWC OSA QMG RCA 1907 ~ 1996

Octobre, La Lièvre, La Salette
oil on canvas, signed and on verso titled
18 x 24 in, 45.7 x 61 cm

PROVENANCE:
Private Collection, Vancouver
Partial proceeds from the sale of this lot will benefit
BC Children's Hospital.

ESTIMATE: $3,000 ~ 4,000

204 CAROLINE HELENA ARMINGTON
1875 ~ 1939

Les Tours de Notre Dame et le Quai aux Fleurs, Paris
oil on canvas, signed and dated 1921
and on verso signed and titled
19 3/4 x 24 in, 50.2 x 61 cm

Caroline Armington studied in Paris at the Académie Julian and the
Académie de la Grande Chaumière, and her paintings were influenced by
the work of the impressionists. In 1900 she married fellow Canadian
artist Frank Armington in Paris, where they lived from 1905 to 1939. She
exhibited in Paris, Canada, London, England and the United States. Her
work was better known outside of Canada and was in the collection of
many museums, and her paintings were highly regarded in her lifetime by
contemporary artists and critics.

ESTIMATE: $12,000 ~ 15,000

205 HENRY GEORGE GLYDE
ASA RCA 1906 ~ 1998

Wharf at Ganges, Salt Spring Island, BC
oil on artist board, signed and on verso signed and titled
16 x 19 3/4 in, 40.6 x 50.2 cm

PROVENANCE:
Hollander York Gallery, Toronto
Private Collection, Toronto

ESTIMATE: $2,000 ~ 2,500

206 JOHN GOODWIN LYMAN
CAS CGP FRSA 1886 ~ 1967

The House by the Sea, Bermuda
oil on canvas, signed and on verso titled
20 x 30 in, 50.8 x 76.2 cm

PROVENANCE:
Dominion Gallery, Montreal
Private Collection, Montreal

ESTIMATE: $10,000 ~ 15,000

207 ALBERT HENRY ROBINSON
ARCA RCA 1881 ~ 1956

Montreal Harbour
oil on panel, signed and dated 1920
8 1/2 x 10 1/2 in, 21.6 x 26.7 cm

PROVENANCE:
George H. Robinson, Toronto, brother of the Artist
By descent to the present Private Collection, Toronto

ESTIMATE: $10,000 ~ 15,000

208 ROBERT GENN
1936 ~

The Baths at Baranoff
oil on canvas, signed and on verso
signed, titled and dated 1978
30 x 36 in, 76.2 x 91.4 cm

PROVENANCE:
Private Collection, Ontario

ESTIMATE: $3,000 ~ 4,000

209 LAWREN STEWART HARRIS
BCSFA G7 OSA PRCA 1885 ~ 1970

Wooden Sketch and Paint Box
paint box, initialed LH and on verso initialed LH
13 3/4 x 11 in, 34.9 x 27.9 cm

PROVENANCE:
A gift to a Private Collector, St. Thomas, Ontario, by Howard Harris, son
of Lawren S. Harris
Acquired by a Private Ontario Collector

ESTIMATE: $3,000 ~ 4,000

210

211

210 A.J. (ALFRED JOSEPH) CASSON
CSPWC G7 POSA PRCA 1898 ~ 1992

Rouge River, Quebec

oil on panel, signed and on verso signed, titled,
dated 1969 and inscribed *below Harrington*
12 x 15 in, 30.5 x 38.1 cm

PROVENANCE:
Roberts Gallery, Toronto
Private Collection, Vancouver

LITERATURE:
Paul Duval, *A.J. Casson*, Roberts Gallery, 1975, page 151

In 1958, Casson retired from his long career at the commercial art firm of
Sampson~Matthews to devote himself full time to his painting. The
Ontario countryside was his usual painting grounds, but in 1966, he
turned his attention to Quebec. Duval writes, "Casson was persuaded at
last to paint in Quebec by A.Y. Jackson, who almost forty years earlier had
failed to convince his younger colleague to sketch among the French
Canadian villages." For six consecutive summers, Casson and Jackson
stayed as guests of Munroe and Joyce Putnam. Duval writes, "From there,
the two artists sketched in the surrounding countryside, sometimes
together, but often alone. Jackson gave Casson the benefit of his intimate
knowledge of the area...Near to Grenville were Harrington, Avoca and
Montebellow, all ideal landscape sites."

By 1969, Casson was experiencing considerable commercial success and
media attention through his Roberts Gallery dealer. Enthusiastic
collectors lined up to purchase his work, and shows were sold out, all of
which was a gratifying experience for Casson. Soon to follow would be a
renewal of interest in the importance of the Group of Seven as Group
members passed away, leaving Casson as the spokesperson for this
important era.

ESTIMATE: $12,000 ~ 16,000

211 A.Y. (ALEXANDER YOUNG) JACKSON
CGP G7 OSA RCA RSA 1882 ~ 1974

Marsh Land, Combermere, Ont.

oil on canvas, signed and on verso
signed, titled and dated 1962
20 x 26 in, 50.8 x 66 cm

PROVENANCE:
Private Collection, BC

LITERATURE:
Naomi Jackson Groves, *A.Y.'s Canada*, 1968, page 98

Combermere is in the Madawaska Valley, east of Algonquin Park. Groves
writes, "A part of Ontario that has retained many features of early days,
and has provided A.Y. with plenty of good subjects, is the hilly, rocky,
wooded, river~and~lake~filled area north of Madoc and Marmora,
familiar names in Ontario's early mining history. Algonquin Park lies to
the northwest of this region, which is usually referred to as the
Madawaska Valley. A.Y. has worked the area for many years, using either
Lake Clear or Combermere as headquarters and driving with friends 'Dr.
Bob' Starrs or Ralph Burton to find good sketching spots. He likes it both
in spring and fall."

This work displays the rugged vigour of this land, and A.Y.'s characteristic
sense of rhythm in the land through the rolling hills in the background
and the bend of bare branches and tree trunks. The painting has a fine
balance between the cool blues of the standing water and sky and the rich
pinks of the clouds and orange hills.

ESTIMATE: $25,000 ~ 35,000

212

214

212   A.Y. (ALEXANDER YOUNG) JACKSON
CGP G7 OSA RCA RSA   1882 ~ 1974

Mitchell Island, Lake Athabaska
(Autumn, Northern Saskatchewan)
oil on panel, signed and on verso signed,
titled and dated September 1957
10 1/2 x 13 1/2 in, 26.7 x 34.3 cm

PROVENANCE:
Private Collection, Toronto

EXHIBITED:
Women's Committee Exhibition, Toronto

ESTIMATE: $8,000 ~ 10,000

214   A.Y. (ALEXANDER YOUNG) JACKSON
CGP G7 OSA RCA RSA   1882 ~ 1974

Northern Bush, Saskatchewan
oil on panel laid down on plywood, signed
10 1/2 x 13 1/2 in, 26.7 x 34.3 cm

PROVENANCE:
Private Collection, Toronto

ESTIMATE: $8,000 ~ 10,000

213   HOMER RANSFORD WATSON
OSA PRCA   1855 ~ 1936

Gathering Storm
oil on board, signed and on verso titled and certified by Rm.
Hamilton for the executors, estate of Homer Watson on a label
10 x 14 in, 25.4 x 35.6 cm

PROVENANCE:
Estate of the Artist, #81~383
Mrs. T.W. Hall
Acquired in 1937 by the present Private Collector, Ontario

ESTIMATE: $7,000 ~ 9,000

213

215

218

216

219

217

220

215 CARL FELLMAN SCHAEFER
OSA RCA 1903 ~ 1995

Birds' Nests

watercolour on paper, signed and
on verso titled and dated Feb. 5, 1955
12 1/2 x 18 in, 31.7 x 45.7 cm

PROVENANCE:
Private Collection, Vancouver

The proceeds of this sale will benefit the programs of the
Vancouver Art Gallery.

ESTIMATE: $1,000 ~ 1,200

216 MOLLY JOAN LAMB BOBAK
BCSFA RCA 1922 ~

Stanley Park

oil on board, signed and dated 1956
23 1/2 x 31 in, 59.7 x 78.7 cm

PROVENANCE:
Acquired by the present Private Toronto Collector, 1957

ESTIMATE: $3,500 ~ 4,500

217 LIONEL LEMOINE FITZGERALD
CGP G7 1890 ~ 1956

Sunlit House

oil on canvas on board, initialed, circa 1920
6 1/4 x 8 in, 15.9 x 20.3 cm

PROVENANCE:
Lionel Lemoine FitzGerald's daughter, Patricia Morrison, Toronto
Private Collection, Toronto

FitzGerald's career had three distinct high points, the first being around
1920 when he mastered a painterly, light~filled technique that looked
back to impressionism. During this period, however, he also painted a
number of small, broadly~brushed canvases that push representation to
the limit. While the artist initialed this one, it is unlikely that any of these
experimental canvases were exhibited during his lifetime. They are
among the earliest proto~abstracts painted in Canada.

ESTIMATE: $3,000 ~ 5,000

218 FRANK (FRANZ) HANS JOHNSTON
ARCA CSPWC G7 OSA 1888 ~ 1949

The Valley Road

oil on board, signed and on verso titled
12 x 16 in, 30.5 x 40.6 cm

PROVENANCE:
Private Collection, Quebec

ESTIMATE: $7,000 ~ 9,000

219 A.Y. (ALEXANDER YOUNG) JACKSON
CGP G7 OSA RCA RSA 1882 ~ 1974

Farm at Clontarf, Ontario

oil on panel, signed and on verso
signed, titled and dated 1966
10 1/2 x 13 1/2 in, 26.7 x 34.3 cm

PROVENANCE:
Private Collection, Ontario

ESTIMATE: $10,000 ~ 12,000

220 J.E.H. (JAMES EDWARD HERVEY) MACDONALD
G7 OSA RCA 1873 ~ 1932

Pasture Lane, Thornhill

oil on panel, on verso signed and titled
8 1/2 x 10 1/2 in, 21.6 x 26.7 cm

PROVENANCE:
Warwick Gallery, Vancouver
Galerie Walter Klinkhoff Inc., Montreal
Private Collection, Ontario

LITERATURE:
Paul Duval, The Tangled Garden: The Art of J.E.H. MacDonald, 1978, page 49

J.E.H. MacDonald went to live and paint in Thornhill in 1913. Duval
writes, "'Four Elms,' as MacDonald called the property, also gave him
plenty of scope for his favourite hobby of gardening. More importantly, it
provided him with subject matter for a number of his finest paintings,
including The Tangled Garden." Other Group of Seven members Arthur
Lismer, Frank Johnston, Frederick Varley and Frank Carmichael also
came to live in Thornhill shortly after MacDonald did. This sketch
expresses beautifully the rugged, rural beauty of the area, with energetic
brushstrokes and a pastel colour palette. The pale yellow lane leads your
eye up the hill and along the picket fence, to disappear behind the trees to
the left.

ESTIMATE: $12,000 ~ 16,000

221

223

221   MANLY EDWARD MACDONALD
OSA RCA 1889 ~ 1971

The Old Mill

oil on canvas board, signed
10 1/2 x 13 1/2 in, 26.7 x 34.3 cm

ESTIMATE: $2,500 ~ 3,000

222   A.Y. (ALEXANDER YOUNG) JACKSON
CGP G7 OSA RCA RSA 1882 ~ 1974

Farming, Poltimore, Quebec

oil on panel, signed and on verso titled, dated April 1963
and certified by Naomi Jackson Groves Inventory #57
10 1/2 x 13 1/2 in, 26.7 x 34.3 cm

PROVENANCE:
C.A.G. Matthews
Didi Petrie (A.Y. Jackson's niece)
Private Collection, Montreal

ESTIMATE: $10,000 ~ 15,000

223   A.Y. (ALEXANDER YOUNG) JACKSON
CGP G7 OSA RCA RSA 1882 ~ 1974

Foggy Day, Ste. Marthe, Gaspé

oil on panel, signed and on verso
signed, titled and dated 1953
10 1/2 x 13 1/2 in, 26.7 x 34.3 cm

PROVENANCE:
Wallack Galleries, Ottawa
Private Collection, Ontario

ESTIMATE: $12,000 ~ 15,000

224

224 ALLEN SAPP

RCA 1929 ~

Cooking Over the Fire

oil on canvas, signed
24 x 30 in, 61 x 76.2 cm

PROVENANCE:

Private Collection, Vancouver

Partial proceeds from the sale of this lot will benefit
BC Children's Hospital.

ESTIMATE: $2,000 ~ 3,000

225 A.Y. (ALEXANDER YOUNG) JACKSON

CGP G7 OSA RCA RSA 1882 ~ 1974

Pig Pen, Barry's Bay

oil on panel, signed indistinctly and on verso
signed and titled
10 1/2 x 13 1/2 in, 26.7 x 34.3 cm

PROVENANCE:

By descent to the present Private Collection, Vancouver

ESTIMATE: $8,000 ~ 10,000

226

226 A.J. (ALFRED JOSEPH) CASSON

CSPWC G7 POSA PRCA 1898 ~ 1992

Moon Rise

oil on board, signed and on verso signed,
titled and dated 1956 on the artist's label
12 x 15 in, 30.5 x 38.1 cm

PROVENANCE:

Kensington Fine Art Gallery Limited, Calgary
Private Collection, Toronto

ESTIMATE: $9,000 ~ 12,000

225

227

227 TAKAO TANABE

1926 ~

Bow River

oil on canvas, signed and dated 1957
48 x 26 in, 121.9 x 66 cm

PROVENANCE:
Dorothy Cameron Gallery, Toronto
Acquired by the present Private Toronto Collector
from the Cameron Gallery, 1957

ESTIMATE: $2,500 ~ 3,500

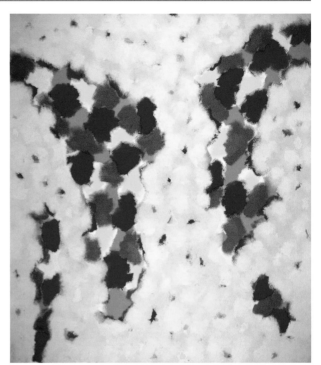

228

228 GERSHON ISKOWITZ

RCA 1921 ~ 1988

New Red Violet ~ D

oil on canvas, on verso signed, titled and dated 1979
50 x 44 in, 127 x 111.7 cm

PROVENANCE:
Gallery Moos, Toronto; Private Collection, Toronto

LITERATURE:
Peter Mellen, Landmarks of Canadian Art, 1978, page 240

Born in Poland, Iskowitz was a survivor of German forced~labour camps
at Auschwitz and Buchenwald. Arriving in Canada in 1949, he explored
Parry Sound in Ontario, and was enamoured of the landscape there. His
style evolved into abstraction, but he still drew on his experiences with
landscape for his work, explaining that that he would take "the
experience, out in the field, of looking up in the trees or in the sky, of
looking down from the height of a helicopter. So what you do is try to
make a composition of all those things, make some kind of reality: like the
trees should belong to the sky, and the ground should belong to the trees,
and the ground should belong to the sky. Everything has to be united." In
1972, international recognition came for his work when he was asked to
represent Canada in the Venice Biennale.

ESTIMATE: $18,000 ~ 24,000

229   ALFRED PELLAN

QMG RCA   1906 ~ 1988

Nature Morte au Canif

oil on paper on board, signed and
on verso titled and inscribed *155*
8 1/4 x 10 1/2 in, 21 x 26.7 cm

PROVENANCE:
Galerie Walter Klinkhoff Inc., Montreal
Waddington & Gorce, Montreal

ESTIMATE: $10,000 ~ 15,000

230   JEAN ALBERT MCEWEN

RCA   1923 ~ 1999

Icon

oil on canvas, on verso signed, circa 1961
12 x 11 in, 30.5 x 27.9 cm

PROVENANCE:
Galerie Agnès Lefort, Montreal
Private Collection, Vancouver

The proceeds of this sale will benefit the programs of the
Vancouver Art Gallery.

ESTIMATE: $3,000 ~ 4,000

229

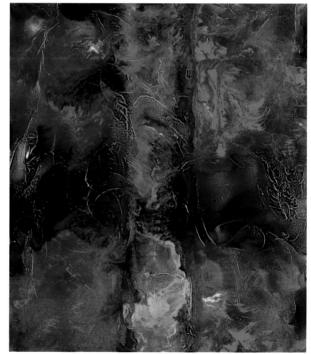

230

Thank you for attending our sale. Please view our *Second Session* May Online Auction of *Fine Canadian Art*
at www.heffel.com, closing on Saturday, May 28, 2005. Lots can be previewed at our Toronto, Montreal or Vancouver offices.

HEFFEL FINE ART AUCTION HOUSE
Auctioneers & Appraisers

VANCOUVER · TORONTO · OTTAWA · MONTREAL

Robert C.S. Heffel   David K.J. Heffel

MONTREAL
1840 Rue Sherbrooke Ouest
Montreal, Quebec H3H 1E4
Telephone 514 939~6505

TORONTO
13 Hazelton Avenue
Toronto, Ontario M5R 2E1
Telephone 416 961~6505

OTTAWA
By appointment
104 Daly Avenue
Ottawa, Ontario K1N 6E7
Telephone 613 230~6505

VANCOUVER
2247 Granville Street
Vancouver, BC V6H 3G1
Telephone 604 732~6505

Canada's national fine art auction house, Heffel's regularly conducts live ballroom auctions of *Fine Canadian Art* in Vancouver during the Spring and Toronto in the Fall, preceded by previews of their sales in Vancouver, Toronto and Montreal. We also conduct monthly Internet auctions of *Fine Canadian, European and American Art*. We have offices in Vancouver, Toronto, Ottawa and Montreal. Our Canadian art experts regularly travel across the country providing free confidential and professional auction appraisals.

Call 1 800 528~9608 today to arrange for the assessment of your fine art for auction or other purposes such as probate, family division or insurance. Our experts can be contacted at any of our locations listed above and you may visit our website at www.heffel.com for further information regarding buying and selling with Heffel's. When you consign with Heffel's your important paintings are marketed globally.

Have you subscribed to Heffel's *Canadian Art at Auction Index?*

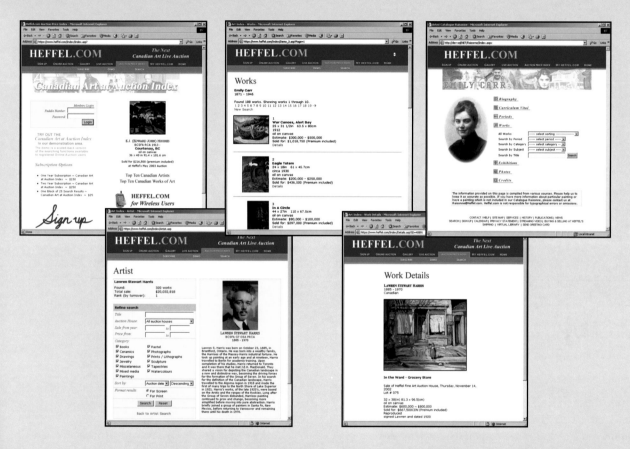

With over 42,000 Lots from Canadian Fine Art Auction Sales,
currently dating back 27 years and expanding monthly,
Heffel's *Canadian Art at Auction Index* is an invaluable resource
for the collector, dealer, appraiser or museum professional

Sign up today online at **www.heffel.com**
or complete our *Subscription Form* on page 139

denbigh design

169 West Seventh Avenue
Vancouver, British Columbia
Canada V5Y 1L8

Telephone: 604•876•3303

Fax: 604•874•0400

Email: denbighdesign@telus.net

Fine Art Services

FRAMING
Custom designed, conservation framing of fine art. Acrylic boxes, stretchers and gilding available.

STORAGE
Secure, temperature controlled storage. Temporary or long term.

TRANSPORT
Door to door service available exclusively for art and antiques - local and long distance

INSTALLATION
Private and corporate installation of art, from single items to entire collections. Exhibition assembly and preparation.

INSURANCE
Transit, shipping and storage insurance available upon request.

CONSERVATION
Fine art conservation services for a wide range of art mediums.

PACKING/CRATING
Custom designed packing containers for all types of art. Standard, touring and museum quality crating.

SHIPPING/RECEIVING
All necessary documentation and shipping arrangements for art - world wide, as well as receiving, unpacking and preparation of condition reports for incoming shipments.

With over 30 years of experience, PACART is dedicated to providing exceptional service and the highest standards of care and attention for the safe and secure transportation of works of art, antiques and precious artifacts.

Toronto
31 Rolark Drive Toronto ON M1R 3B1
Tel: 416 754 0000 Fax: 416 754 2855 email: info@pacart.ca

Montréal
4107 Rue Cousens Montréal QC H4S 1V6
Téléphone: 514 334 5858 Télécopieur: 514 334 5006 courriel: pacartquebec@pacart.ca

Printing so good you won't be able to control yourself.

There's nothing quite like the feeling you get when you find yourself at a press check and everything's just perfect. Sometimes emotions can just take over. And we're okay with that. We've built Generation to meet the creative and technical challenges you face today; with the latest equipment, expert staff and the resources to do what it takes to surpass your expectations. So go ahead, give us a squeeze.

Feel the love.

generation
PRINTING

31 West 3rd Avenue, Vancouver, BC V5Y 3T8 Tel: 604.254.4488 Fax: 604.254.0408
Toll Free: 866.334.4488 www.generationprinting.com

on newsstands now

PLEASE VISIT US IN MONTREAL AND TORONTO FOR OUR MAY AUCTION HIGHLIGHT PREVIEWS

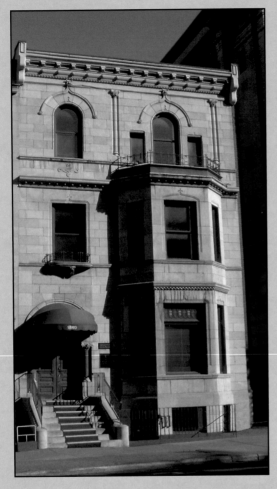

Montreal *Evening Vernissage* Wednesday, May 4, 7pm to 9pm
Montreal Preview Thursday, May 5, through Saturday, May 7, 11am to 6pm
Toronto Preview Wednesday, May 11, through Saturday, May 14, 11am to 6pm

Please visit our live auction online catalogue at www.heffel.com for specific details designating which Lots will be available for our Montreal and Toronto previews

1840 RUE SHERBROOKE OUEST
MONTREAL, QUEBEC H3H 1E4
TELEPHONE: 514 939~6505
TOLL FREE: 866 939~6505
FACSIMILE: 514 939~1100

13 HAZELTON AVENUE
TORONTO, ONTARIO M5R 2E1
TELEPHONE: 416 961~6505
TOLL FREE: 866 961~6505
FACSIMILE: 416 961~4245

TERMS AND CONDITIONS OF BUSINESS

These Terms and Conditions of Business represent the terms upon which the Auction House contracts with the Consignor and, acting in its capacity as agent on behalf of the Consignor, contracts with the Purchaser. These Terms and Conditions of Business shall apply to the sale of the Lot by the Auction House to the Purchaser on behalf of the Consignor, and shall supersede and take precedence over any previously agreed Terms and Conditions of Business. These Terms and Conditions of Business are hereby incorporated into and form part of the Consignment Agreement entered into by the Auction House and the Consignor.

A DEFINED TERMS:

1 LOT
Any property delivered by the Consignor to the Auction House to be placed in the auction sale held by the Auction House on its premises or elsewhere, and specifically that property described by Lot number in the Auction House catalogue for the auction sale.

2 RESERVE
The confidential minimum price established between the Auction House and the Consignor. The reserve will not exceed the low estimate as published in our catalogue.

3 KNOCKED DOWN
The conclusion of the sale of the Lot being auctioned by the Auctioneer.

4 HAMMER PRICE
The price at which the Auctioneer Knocked Down the Lot to the Purchaser.

5 PURCHASER
The person, corporation or other entity or such entity's agent, who bids successfully on the Lot at the auction.

6 PURCHASE PRICE
The Hammer Price plus any premium, GST/HST and PST chargeable and additional charges and expenses including any charges and expenses due from a defaulting Purchaser as set out in this Agreement.

7 PURCHASER'S PREMIUM
The Auction House rate of the Purchaser's Premium is 15% of the Hammer Price of each Lot.

8 GST/HST
The Goods and Services Tax / Harmonized Sales Tax levied and exigible pursuant to the *Excise Tax Act*, RSC 1985, and the regulations thereunder, as amended from time to time.

9 PST
Provincial Sales Tax levied and exigible pursuant to the *Social Services Tax Act*, RSBC 1979, Chap. 388, and the regulations thereunder, as amended from time to time.

10 PROCEEDS OF SALE
The net amount due to the Consignor from the Auction House, which shall be the Hammer Price less commission at the Published Rates and Expenses and any other amounts due to the Auction House or to any associated company of the Auction House from the Consignor.

B THE PURCHASER:

1 THE AUCTION HOUSE
The Auction House acts solely as agent for the Consignor, except as otherwise provided herein.

2 THE PURCHASER
(a) The highest bidder acknowledged by the Auctioneer as the highest bidder at the time the Lot is Knocked Down;

(b) The Auctioneer has the right, at his sole discretion, to reopen a Lot if he has inadvertently missed a Bid, or if a Bidder immediately at the close of a Lot notifies the Auctioneer of his intent to Bid;

(c) The Auctioneer shall have the right to regulate and control the bidding and to advance the bids in whatever intervals he considers appropriate for the Lot in question;

(d) The Auction House shall have absolute discretion in settling any dispute in determining the successful bidder;

(e) Every bidder shall be deemed to act as principal unless the Auction House has acknowledged in writing prior to the date of the auction that the bidder is acting as agent on behalf of a disclosed principal and where such disclosure is acceptable to the Auction House; and,

(f) The Purchaser acknowledges that invoices generated during the sale or shortly after may not be error~free, and therefore are subject to review;

(g) Every bidder shall sign a Registration Form and provide appropriate identification to the Auction House.

3 PURCHASER'S PREMIUM
The Purchaser shall pay the Auction House the Purchaser's Premium of 15% of the Hammer Price of each Lot, together with applicable GST/HST and PST, unless a valid PST Exempt number is presented to the Auction House prior to the auction sale. The Purchaser acknowledges that the Auction House may also receive commission from the Consignor in accordance with the provisions of this Agreement.

4 GOODS
GST/HST and PST are exigible on all Auction House transactions. The GST/HST and PST may be refundable in part in certain circumstances if the Lot is delivered outside or removed from British Columbia. Where the Purchaser can demonstrate, to the satisfaction of the Auction House, that such delivery and/or removal is in compliance with the provisions of the relevant GST/HST and PST legislation, the refund may apply in whole or in part.

5 **PAYMENT OF THE PURCHASE PRICE**

(a) The Purchaser shall:

   (i) unless he has already done so, provide the Auction House with his name, address and banking or other suitable references; and,

   (ii) pay the Auction House the Purchase Price within seven days from the date of the sale. Payment shall be made by Certified Cheque or Bank Draft, unless otherwise arranged in advance with the Auction House. A cheque must be accompanied by a current Letter of Credit from the Purchaser's bank which will guarantee the amount of the cheque. A cheque not guaranteed by a Letter of Credit must be cleared by the Banks *approximately ten days* prior to purchases being released. VISA or Mastercard payments must not exceed $25,000.

(b) Subject to the provisions of this Agreement, the title to the property in a Lot shall not pass to the Purchaser until the Purchaser has paid the Purchase Price in full to the Auction House.

6 **DESCRIPTIONS OF LOT**

(a) All representations or statements made by the Auction House, or in the Consignment Agreement, or in the catalogue or other publication or report, as to the authorship, origin, date, age, size, medium, attribution, genuineness, provenance, condition or estimated selling price of the Lot, is a statement of opinion only;

(b) All photographic representations and other illustrations presented in the catalogue are solely for guidance and are not to be relied upon in terms of tone or colour or necessarily to reveal any imperfections in the Lot;

(c) Many Lots are of an age or nature which precludes their being in pristine condition. Some descriptions in the catalogue or given by way of condition report make reference to damage and/or restoration. Such information is given for guidance only and the absence of such a reference does not imply that a Lot is free from defects, nor does any reference to particular defects imply the absence of others; and,

(d) The Purchaser must satisfy himself as to the matters referred to in (a), (b) and (c) of this paragraph by inspection or otherwise prior to the sale of the Lot.

7 **PURCHASED LOT**

(a) Prior to any Lot being removed from the premises of the Auction House, the Purchaser shall pay to the Auction House the full purchase price;

(b) The Purchaser shall collect the Lot from the Auction House within seven (7) days from the date of the auction sale, after which date the Purchaser shall be responsible for all storage charges until the date the Lot is removed from the offices of the Auction House;

(c) All packing and handling of the purchased Lots by the Auction House staff is undertaken solely as a service to the Purchaser, and will only be undertaken at the discretion of the Auction House and at the Purchaser's risk;

(d) The Auction House shall not be liable for any damage to glass or frames of the Lot and shall not be liable for any errors or omissions or damage caused by packers and shippers, notwithstanding the fact that the Auction House may have recommended such shippers or packers to the Purchaser.

8 **RISK**

(a) The purchased Lot shall be at the Purchaser's risk in all respects from the time of collection or on the expiration of seven days (7) from the date of sale, whichever is earlier.

(b) Neither the Auction House nor its employees nor its agents shall be liable for any loss or damage of any kind to the Property after the expiration of the seven days (7) from the date of sale, whether caused by negligence or otherwise, while any Lot is in or under the respective custody or control of the Auction House.

9 **NONPAYMENT AND FAILURE TO COLLECT LOT(S)**

If the Purchaser fails either to pay for or to take away any Lot within seven (7) days from the date of the auction sale, the Auction House may in its absolute discretion be entitled to one or more of the following remedies without providing further notice to the Purchaser and without prejudice to any other rights or remedies the Auction House may have:

(a) To issue judicial proceedings against the Purchaser for damages for breach of contract together with the costs of such proceedings on a full indemnity basis;

(b) To rescind the sale of that or any other Lots sold to the Purchaser;

(c) To resell the Lot or cause it to be resold by public or private sale, with any such deficiency to be claimed from the Purchaser and any surplus, after Expenses, to be delivered to the Purchaser;

(d) To store the Lot on the premises of the Auction House or elsewhere, and to release the Lot to the Purchaser only after payment of the full Purchase Price and associated cost to the Auction House;

(e) To charge interest on the Purchase Price at the rate of 5% above the Royal Bank of Canada base rate at the time of the auction sale and adjusted month to month thereafter;

(f) To retain that or any other Lot sold to the Purchaser at the same or any other auction and release the same only after payment of the Purchase Price;

(g) To apply any Proceeds of Sale of any Lot then due or at any time thereafter becoming due to the Purchaser towards settlement of the Purchase Price, and the Auction House shall be entitled to a lien on any other property of the Purchaser which is in the Auction House possession for any purpose; and,

(h) To apply any payments by the Purchaser to the Auction House towards any sums owing from the Purchaser to the Auction House or to any associated company of the Auction House without regard to any directions of the Purchaser or his agent, whether express or implied.

10 GUARANTEE

The Consignor, the Auction House, its employees and agents, although every effort has been made for accuracy, shall not be responsible for the correctness of any statement as to the authorship, origin, date, age, size, medium, attribution, genuineness or provenance of any Lot or for any other errors of description or for any faults or defects in any Lot and no warranty whatsoever is given by the Consignor, the Auction House, its employees or agents in respect of any Lot and any express or implied conditions or warranties are hereby excluded.

11 ATTENDANCE BY PURCHASER

(a) Prospective Purchasers are strongly advised to inspect the Lots before the sale, and to satisfy themselves as to the description, attribution and condition of each Lot. To this end the Auction House will arrange suitable viewing conditions during the Preview preceding the sale itself, or by private appointment.

(b) Prospective Purchasers are also advised to personally attend the sale. However, if they are unable to attend, the Auction House will execute bids on their behalf provided that notice of such bids is set out on the proper Absentee Bid Form found at the back of the sale catalogue, duly signed and delivered to the Auction House preferably twenty~four (24) hours before the start of the auction sale. The Auction House intends this as a service, free of charge, to Prospective Purchasers, but accepts no responsibility whatsoever or liability in the making of any such bid by its employees or agents;

(c) In the event that the Auction House has received more than one Absentee Bid Form on a Lot for an identical amount and at auction those absentee bids are the highest bids for that Lot, the Lot shall be Knocked Down to the person whose Absentee Bid Form was received first;

(d) At the discretion of the Auction House, and subject to limited availability, the Auction House may execute bids, if appropriately instructed by telephone, on behalf of the Prospective Purchaser, and the Prospective Purchaser hereby agrees that neither the Auction House nor its employees nor agents shall be liable to either the Purchaser or the Consignor for any neglect or default in making such a bid.

12 EXPORT PERMITS

Without limitation, the Purchaser acknowledges that certain property of Canadian cultural import sold by the Auction House may be subject to the provisions of the *Cultural Property Import and Export Act of Canada*, and that compliance with the provisions of the said Act is the sole responsibility of the Purchaser.

C THE CONSIGNOR:

1 THE AUCTION HOUSE

(a) The Auction House shall have absolute discretion as to whether the Lot is suitable for sale, the particular auction sale for the Lot, the date of the auction sale, the manner in which the auction sale is conducted, the catalogue descriptions of the Lot, and any other matters related to the sale of the Lot at the auction sale;

(b) The Auction House reserves the right to withdraw any Lot at any time prior to the auction sale if, in the sole discretion of the Auction House:

   (i) there is doubt as to its authenticity;

   (ii) there is doubt as to the accuracy of the Consignor's representations or warranties set forth herein;

   (iii) the Consignor has breached or is about to breach any provisions of this Agreement; or

   (iv) any other just cause exists.

(c) In the event of a withdrawal pursuant to Condition C.1.b.(ii) or C.1.b.(iii), the Consignor shall pay a charge to the Auction House, as provided in Condition C.8.

2 WARRANTIES AND INDEMNITIES

(a) The Consignor warrants to the Auction House and to the Purchaser that the Consignor has and shall be able to deliver unencumbered title to the Lot, free from all third~party rights or claims;

(b) The Consignor shall indemnify the Auction House, its employees and agents and the Purchaser against all claims made or proceedings brought by persons entitled or purporting to be entitled to the Lot;

(c) The Consignor shall indemnify the Auction House, its employees and agents and the Purchaser against all claims made or proceedings brought due to any default of the Consignor in complying with any applicable legislation, regulations or requirements; and,

(d) The Consignor shall reimburse the Auction House in full and on demand for all payments, costs, expenses or any other loss or damage whatsoever made, incurred or suffered as a result of any breach by the Consignor of C.2.a and/or C.2.c above.

3   RESERVES

(a) All Reserves shall be in the lawful currency of Canada as agreed in writing between the Consignor and the Auction House.

(b) The Auction House is authorized by the Consignor to Knock Down a Lot at less than the Reserve, provided that, for the purposes of calculating the Proceeds of Sale due to the Consignor, the Hammer Price shall be deemed to be the full amount of the agreed Reserve established by the Auction House and the Consignor.

4   COMMISSION AND EXPENSES

(a) The Consignor authorizes the Auction House to deduct the Consignor's Commission and Expenses from the Hammer Price and, notwithstanding that the Auction House is the Consignor's agent, acknowledges that the Auction House shall retain the Purchaser's Premium; and,

(b) The Consignor shall pay and authorizes the Auction House to deduct all Expenses incurred on behalf of the Consignor, together with any GST/HST and PST thereon; and,

(c) The charge for illustrating a Lot in the auction sale catalogue shall be a flat fee paid by the Consignor of $500 for a large size reproduction and $275 for a small reproduction, per piece of art, together with any GST/HST and PST chargeable thereon. The Auction House retains all rights to photographic and printing material and the right of reproduction of such photographs.

5   INSURANCE

(a) All Lots shall be covered by insurance under the Fine Arts Insurance Policy of the Auction House;

(b) The rate of insurance premium payable by the Consignor is $15 per $1,000 of the high pre~sale estimate;

(c) If the Consignor instructs the Auction House not to insure a Lot, it shall at all times remain at the risk of the Consignor who hereby undertakes to:

   (i) indemnify the Auction House against all claims made or proceedings brought against the Auction House in respect of loss or damage to the Lot of whatever nature, howsoever and wheresoever occurred, and in any circumstances even where negligence is alleged or proven;

   (ii) reimburse the Auction House on demand for all Expenses incurred or suffered by the Auction House. Any payment which the Auction House shall make in respect of such loss or damage or payments, costs or Expenses shall be binding upon the Consignor and shall be accepted by the Consignor as conclusive evidence that the Auction House was liable to make such payment; and,

   (iii) notify any insurer of the existence of the indemnity contained in this Condition;

(d) The Auction House does not accept responsibility for Lots damaged by changes in atmospheric conditions and the Auction House shall not be liable for such damage nor for any other damage to picture frames or to glass in picture frames; and,

(e) The sum for which a Lot is insured under the Fine Arts Policy of the Auction House in accordance with subclause C.4.b. above shall be the total amount due to the Consignor in the event of a successful claim being made under the Fine Arts Policy.

6   PAYMENT OF PROCEEDS OF SALE

(a) The Auction House shall pay the Proceeds of Sale to the Consignor thirty~five (35) days after the date of sale, if the Auction House has been paid the Purchase Price in full by the Purchaser;

(b) If by the due date the Auction House has not received the Purchase Price in full from the Purchaser, then the Auction House will pay the Proceeds of Sale within seven (7) working days after the date on which the Purchase Price in full is received from the Purchaser; and,

(c) If before the Purchase Price is paid in full by the Purchaser, the Auction House pays the Consignor an amount equal to the Proceeds of Sale, title to the property in the Lot shall pass to the Auction House.

7   COLLECTION OF THE PURCHASE PRICE

If the Purchaser fails to pay to the Auction House the Purchase Price within one month after the date of sale, the Auction House will endeavour to take the Consignor's instructions as to the appropriate course of action to be taken and, so far as in the Auction House opinion such instructions are practicable, will assist the Consignor in recovering the Purchase price from the Purchaser, save that the Auction House shall not be obligated to issue judicial proceedings against the Purchaser in its own name. Notwithstanding the foregoing, the Auction House reserves the right and is hereby authorized at the Consignor's expense, and in each case at the absolute discretion of the Auction House, to agree to special terms for payment of the Purchase Price, to remove, store and insure the Lot sold, to settle claims made by or against the Purchaser on such terms as the Auction House shall think fit, to take such steps as are necessary to collect monies from the Purchaser to the Consignor and, if appropriate, to set aside the sale and refund money to the Purchaser.

8   CHARGES FOR WITHDRAWN LOTS

The Consignor may not withdraw a Lot prior to the auction without the consent of the Auction House. In the event that such consent is given, or in the event of a withdrawal pursuant to Condition C.1.b.ii or iii, a charge of 20% of the high pre~sale estimate or, if no pre~sale estimate has yet been agreed, a charge of 20% of the figure at which the Lot has been valued for insurance as determined by the Auction House together with any GST/HST and PST chargeable thereon and Expenses shall become payable to the Auction House.

9 Unsold Lots

(a) Unsold Lots must be collected at the Consignor's expense within the period of ninety (90) days after receipt by the Consignor of notice from the Auction House. Upon the expiration of such a period, the Auction House shall have the right to sell such Lots by public or private sale and on such terms as it thinks fit and to deduct from the Proceeds of Sale any sum owing to the Auction House or to any associated company of the Auction House including Expenses on the sale of the Lots and all other Expenses before remitting the balance to the Consignor. If the Consignor cannot be traced, the Auction House shall place the funds in a bank account in the name of the Auction House for the Consignor. In this Condition the expression "Proceeds of Sale" shall have the same meaning in relation to a sale by private treaty as it has in relation to a sale by auction;

(b) Lots returned at the Consignor's request shall be returned at the Consignor's risk and expense and will not be insured in transit unless the Auction House is otherwise instructed by the Consignor; and,

(c) If any Lot is unsold by auction, the Auction House is authorized as the exclusive agent for the Consignor for a period of three months following the auction to sell such Lot privately for a price that will result in a payment to the Consignor of not less than the net amount, *i.e., after deduction of the Auction House Commission and Expenses,* to which the Consignor would have been entitled had the Lot been sold at a price equal to the agreed Reserve, or for such lesser amount as the Auction House and the Consignor shall agree. In such event the Consignor's obligations to the Auction House hereunder with respect to such a Lot are the same as if it had been sold at auction.

10 Consignor's GST/HST Status

The Consignor shall give to the Auction House all relevant information as to his GST/HST status with regard to the Lot to be sold, which he warrants is and will be correct and upon which the Auction House shall be entitled to rely.

11 Photographs and Illustrations

The Consignor hereby grants to the Auction House the exclusive right to illustrate and photograph any Lot given to the Auction House by the Consignor for sale, and to use such photographs, illustrations or images therefrom, and any illustration, photographs or images provided by the Consignor to the Auction House, at any time and for such purposes as it sees fit, whether such purposes are related to the sale of the Lot in question or not.

D GENERAL CONDITIONS:

1 The Auction House as agent for the Consignor is not responsible for any default by the Consignor or the Purchaser.

2 The Auction House shall have the right at its absolute discretion to refuse admission to its premises or attendance at its auctions by any person.

3 The Auction House has the right at its absolute discretion to refuse any bid, to advance the bidding as it may decide, to withdraw or divide any Lot, to combine any two or more Lots and, in the case of dispute, to put up any Lot for auction again.

4 Any indemnity hereunder shall extend to all actions, proceedings, costs, claims and demands whatsoever incurred or suffered by the person for whose benefit the indemnity is given; and the Auction House shall hold any indemnity on trust for its employees and agents where it is expressed to be for their benefit.

5 Any notice given hereunder shall be in writing and if given by post shall be deemed to have been duly received by the addressee within three (3) business days.

6 The copyright for all illustrations and written matter relating to the Lots shall be and will remain at all times the absolute property of the Auction House and shall not, without the prior written consent of the Auction House, be used by any other person.

7 This Agreement shall be governed by and construed in accordance with British Columbia law and the federal laws of Canada applicable therein and all parties concerned hereby submit to the non~exclusive jurisdiction of the British Columbian Courts.

8 Unless otherwise provided for herein, all monetary amounts referred to herein shall refer to the lawful money of Canada.

9 All words importing the singular number shall include the plural and vice versa, and words importing the use of any gender shall include the masculine, feminine and neuter genders and the word "person" shall include an individual, a trust, a partnership, a body corporate, an association or other incorporated or unincorporated organization or entity.

The Purchaser and the Consignor are hereby advised to read fully the Agreement which sets out and establishes the rights and obligations of the Auction House, the Purchaser and the Consignor and the terms by which the Auction House shall conduct the sale and handle other related matters.

CATALOGUE TERMS:

These catalogue terms are provided for your guidance:

Cornelius David Krieghoff
In our best judgment, a work by the artist.

Attributed to Cornelius David Krieghoff
In our best judgment, a work executed in whole or in part by the named artist.

Studio of Cornelius David Krieghoff
In our best judgment, a work by an unknown hand in the studio of the artist, possibly executed under the supervision of the named artist.

Circle of Cornelius David Krieghoff
In our best judgment, a work of the period of the artist, closely related to the style of the named artist.

Manner of Cornelius David Krieghoff
In our best judgment, a work in the style of the named artist and of a later date.

After Cornelius David Krieghoff
In our best judgment, a copy of a known work of the named artist.

Dimensions
Measurements are given height before width in both inches and centimetres.

Picture Frames
Pictures are framed unless otherwise noted.

Signed / Titled / Dated
In our best judgment, the work has been signed/titled/dated by the artist. If we state "dated 1856" then the artist has inscribed the date when the work was produced. If the artist has not inscribed the date and we state "1856", then it is known the work was produced in 1856, based on independent research. If the artist has not inscribed the date and there is no independent date reference, then the use of "circa" approximates the date based on style and period.

Bears Signature / Bears Date
In our best judgment, the signature/date is by a hand other than that of the artist.

Provenance
Is intended to indicate previous collections or owners

Certificates / Literature / Exhibited
Any reference to certificates, literature or exhibition history represents the best judgment of the authority or authors named.

Estimate
Our Estimates are intended as a statement of our best judgment only, and represent a conservative appraisal of the expected Hammer Price.

CATALOGUE ABBREVIATIONS AND SYMBOLS:

P	*before Society* indicates President
A	*before Society* indicates Associate Member
AAM	Art Association of Montreal *founded 1860*
ALC	Arts and Letters Club, Vancouver
ASA	Alberta Society of Artists
BCSFA	British Columbia Society of Fine Arts *founded in 1909*
BHHG	Beaver Hall Hill Group, Montreal *1920~1922*
CAC	Canadian Art Club
CGP	Canadian Group of Painters *1933~1969*
CPE	Canadian Painters ~ Etchers' Society
CSAA	Canadian Society of Applied Art
CSGA	Canadian Society of Graphic Artists *founded in 1905*
CSMA	Canadian Society of Marine Artists
CSPWC	Canadian Society of Painters in Watercolour *founded in 1926*
FCA	Federation of Canadian Artists
G7	Group of Seven *1920~1933*
NFAAM	Non~Figurative Artists' Association of Montreal
NSSA	Nova Scotia Society of Artists
OC	Order of Canada
OIP	Ontario Institute of Painters
OSA	Ontario Society of Artists *founded 1872*
P11	Painters Eleven *1953~1960*
RA	Royal Academy
RAIC	Royal Architects Institute of Canada
RBA	Royal Society of British Artists
RCA	Royal Canadian Academy of Arts *founded 1880*
RPS	Royal Photographic Society
RSA	Royal Scottish Academy
SAP	Société des Arts Plastiques
SC	The Studio Club
SCA	Society of Canadian Artists *1867~1872*
TCC	Toronto Camera Club
φ	Indicates the Heffel Gallery owns an equity interest in the Lot
⬚	Denotes that additional information on this lot can be found on our website at www.heffel.com

ANNUAL SUBSCRIPTION FORM

Please complete this Annual Subscription Form to receive our twice~yearly *Auction Catalogues* and *Auction Result Sheet*.

To order, return a copy of this form with a cheque payable to: Heffel Gallery Limited, 2247 Granville Street, Vancouver, British Columbia, Canada V6H 3G1
Tel 604 732~6505, Fax 604 732~4245, Toll free 800 528~9608
E~mail: mail@heffel.com, Internet: http//www.heffel.com

CATALOGUE SUBSCRIPTIONS ~ TAX INCLUDED

DELIVERED IN CANADA

☐ One Year ~ *Fine Canadian Art* $50.00
☐ Two Year ~ *Fine Canadian Art* $75.00

DELIVERED TO THE UNITED STATES AND OVERSEAS

☐ One Year ~ *Fine Canadian Art* $60.00
☐ Two Year ~ *Fine Canadian Art* $100.00

CANADIAN ART AT AUCTION INDEX ONLINE ~ TAX INCLUDED
Please contact the Heffel Gallery to set~up

☐ One Block of 25 Search Results $50.00
☐ One Year Subscription (35 searches per month) $250.00
☐ Two Year Subscription (35 searches per month) $350.00

Name

Address

Postal Code   E~mail Address

Residence Telephone   Business Telephone

Fax   Cellular

VISA # or MasterCard #   Expiry Date

Signature   Date

COLLECTOR PROFILE FORM

Please complete our Collector Profile Form to assist us in our ability to offer you our finest service.

ARTISTS OF PARTICULAR INTEREST IN PURCHASING

1)

2)

3)

4)

5)

6)

7)

8)

9)

ARTISTS OF PARTICULAR INTEREST IN SELLING

1)

2)

3)

4)

5)

6)

7)

8)

9)

SHIPPING FORM FOR PURCHASES

Heffel Fine Art Auction House will arrange to have Property purchased at the auction sale packed, insured and forwarded to the Purchaser at their expense and risk pursuant to the Terms and Conditions of Business set out in the Auction Sale Catalogue. The Purchaser is aware and accepts that Heffel Fine Art Auction House does not operate a professional packing service and shall provide such assistance for the convenience only of the Purchaser. Using its discretion, solely as an accommodation to Purchasers, Heffel Fine Art Auction House will pack, on its premises, small objects that are not fragile and prints in unglassed frames. Larger works will be forwarded to a professional art transport company. Your signature on this form releases Heffel Fine Art Auction House from any liability that may result from damage sustained by artwork during packing and shipping. All such works are packed at the Purchaser's risk and then transported by a carrier chosen at the discretion of Heffel Fine Art Auction House. All packing, handling and shipping charges will be at the Purchaser's expense. Works purchased may be subject to the *Cultural Property Import and Export Act of Canada*, and compliance with the provisions of the said Act is the sole responsibility of the Purchaser.

_____

Sale Date

OPTION ONE

I will collect my purchase ☐ *or* have it collected on my behalf ☐

_____

Individual or company collecting my purchase on my behalf

_____

Date of collection/pick~up

OPTION TWO

Please arrange for the packaging and forwarding of my purchase listed and insure the shipment for full auction sale value ☐

or, please arrange for the packaging and forwarding of my purchase listed and do not insure ☐

Please forward a quote for the above services ☐

ALL CHARGES ARE COLLECT FOR SETTLEMENT BY THE PURCHASER

Forward by ☐ Air Freight ☐ Surface

Carrier ☐ Federal Express ☐ Other _____

Carrier Account Number _____

_____

Purchaser's Name *as invoiced*

_____

Shipping Address

_____

City   Province, Country

_____

Postal Code   E~mail Address

_____

Residence Telephone   Business Telephone

_____

Fax   Cellular

_____

Credit Card Number   Expiry Date

_____

Social Security Number for U.S. Customs (U.S. Resident Only)

_____

Signed with agreement to the above   Date

LOT NUMBER *in numerical order*	LOT DESCRIPTION *artist*
1)	
2)	
3)	
4)	

2247 Granville Street, Vancouver
British Columbia, Canada V6H 3G1
Telephone 604 732~6505, Fax 604 732~4245
E~mail: mail@heffel.com, Internet: http://www.heffel.com

ABSENTEE BID FORM

Sale Date

Billing Name

Address

City   Province, Country

Postal Code   E~mail Address

Daytime Telephone   Evening Telephone

Fax   Cellular

I request Heffel Fine Art Auction House to enter bids on my behalf for the following Lots, up to the maximum Hammer Price I have indicated for each Lot. I understand that if my bid is successful, the purchase price shall be the Hammer Price plus a Purchaser's Premium of 15% of the Hammer Price of each Lot, and applicable GST/HST and PST. I understand that Heffel Fine Art Auction House executes absentee bids as a convenience for its clients and is not responsible for inadvertently failing to execute bids or for errors relating to their execution of my bids. On my behalf, Heffel Fine Art Auction House will try to purchase these Lots for the lowest possible price, taking into account the reserve and other bids. If identical absentee bids are received, Heffel Fine Art Auction House will give precedence to the Absentee Bid Form received first. I understand and acknowledge all successful bids are subject to the Terms and Conditions of Business printed in the Heffel Fine Art Auction House catalogue.

Signature   Date

Date Received ~ for office use only

Confirmed ~ for office use only

Please view our General Bidding Increments found on page 5.

LOT NUMBER	LOT DESCRIPTION	MAXIMUM BID
in numerical order	*artist*	*Hammer Price $ CDN (excluding Purchaser's Premium)*
1)		
2)		
3)		
4)		
5)		
6)		
7)		
8)		

To be sure that bids will be accepted and delivery of lots not delayed, bidders not yet known to Heffel Fine Art Auction House should supply a bank reference. All Absentee Bidders must supply a valid Mastercard or VISA # and expiry date.

MasterCard or VISA #   Expiry Date

Name of Bank   Branch

Address of Bank

Name of Account Officer   Telephone

To allow time for processing, absentee bids should be received at least 24 hours before the sale begins. Heffel Fine Art Auction House will confirm all bids received by fax by return fax. If you have not received our confirmation within one business day, please re~submit your bids or contact David or Robert Heffel at:

2247 Granville Street, Vancouver
British Columbia, Canada V6H 3G1
Telephone 604 732~6505, Fax 604 732~4245
E~mail: mail@heffel.com; Internet: http://www.heffel.com

INDEX OF ARTISTS BY LOT

T/U/V/W/X/Y/Z

In memory of

PETER NOEL LAWSON (WINTERHALTER) ASPELL

December 25, 1918 ~ December 28, 2004

**DAVID BONAR BLACKWOOD
(DAVID JUDAH)**

July 12, 1971 ~ March 10, 2005